ANGST

Hélène Cixous

ANGST

Translated from the French by
Jo Levy

JOHN CALDER · LONDON
RIVERRUN PRESS · NEW YORK

First published in English in Great Britain in 1985 by
John Calder (Publishers) Ltd
18 Brewer Street
London W1R 4AS
and first published in the U.S.A. in 1985 by
Riverrun Press Inc.,
175 Fifth Avenue
New York, NY 10001

Originally published in France as *Angst* in 1977 by
Editions des Femmes
2 rue de la Roquette, 75011 Paris

British Library Cataloguing in Publication Data
Cixous, Hélène
    Angst.
    I. Title   II. Angst. *English*
    843'.914[F]   PQ2663.I9

    ISBN 0-7145-3905-8

Library of Congress Cataloging in Publication Data
Cixous, Hélène, 1937—
    Angst.
    I. T.
    PQ2663.I9A813   1985   843'.914   85-18296
    ISBN 0-7145-3905-8 (pbk.)

Photoset in 11/12 Baskerville and printed in Great Britain by
Photobooks (Bristol) Ltd

to the Vital woman, to whom this text did not know it would lead . . .

The worst is upon me. This is it: the scene of Great Suffering. During this scene the impossible takes place: my death attacks me, life panics and splits in two; one life tears at the other which has it by the throat, biting. You struggle. The body breaks, the sky shatters, the scene bursts into flames. You fall and the earth is no longer there.

Suddenly you know: all is lost. Everything. Suddenly all is known. No more scene, yet no end. Cut. You say I. And I bleed. I am outside. Bleeding. Yet formless, helpless, almost bodiless. In and out of my body. In pain. Here, I no longer have what I once had; you no longer know what you once knew. You're not there any more. Outside, frozen. Motionless. Deported. Displaced. I still want to have; I still want to be able. Attacked. I want to be on the way to love. To death. To hold on to what is going to disappear. Still losing. Not dead, worse. The body, here. Separate. Flesh: separation. Head icy-cold. Cries caught in silence. Here, all is silence; there, noises flow. Dried up. Nothing left. Except the suffering flesh. Existing for no one: I am the being who exists for no-body. As if the hands from On High had opened. Fallen out of life, like a thunderbolt; hurled from the heights of love. Below, the heart, even warmer than before, is shaken, tortured unable to flee. The heart is imprisoned down below; your own hands crush it in the chest between harsh fingers. Claws.

7

Not destroyed, not killed, worse. The worst: bereft. Not heard. Who would you shout for? No longer desired. No longer touched. Expelled. Out of reach. I am nowhere. The body, here, with no address. A being who has stopped having: the impossible is here possible. My body: suffering surviving in a savage ring round the heart.

Life wasn't delivered to me yesterday. It didn't come today. No one to send it—space breaks up during this scene; what held together falls apart—No life delivered. No letter. Nowhere to come to, here. Things happen, but not here. You've lost the right to go where things happen. You're no longer in the know. Suddenly: there's no more inside!—except the heart, clawed. Out there: possessions, house, eyes, names, ears, gestures move and touch; speech carries, letters are sent and read—impossible. The impossible: day breaks, somewhere. There's sense—air—meaning flowing through the earth, flavouring it. It goes out, climbs trees, makes streets roll on, gets cities to wake up, gets people to come in, go to bed. Here: no more inside, everything is outside—except the cries for no one, crushed, stifled between clenched teeth. And outside: no way-out. Suddenly you know what you did not know: you are flung out into no-man's land, and there's no way out, ever.

Where no one calls you.

You don't arrive here. No road leads nowhere. Death fell upon me, in the dark; you fought. I struggled. I'm sure it's the scene that let go of me. Life let me down. The hands had abandoned me.

Here is the unprecedented scene:

My mother puts me down on the ground. The room closes in. 'Wait there for me. I'll be back straightaway.' My mother goes out. The ground closes in. I am outside. When *I* am not there *you* die. Betrayed. Everything starts to die.

The soul has shattered. You lose your senses. What couldn't happen has happened to me. Who put me down?

8

My mother whom I trust—the ground for this scene was covered with strange tiles: yellow bits, all stuck together—Everything holds together, the ground is still there. As soon as I am put down I begin to shudder; I am still trusting, sense buzzes in my ears. It was summer. The room held me tightly. The light goes out. The sky dies on me. Who's pounding the ground in the dark, smashing it with a hammer, scattering the pieces? And straightaway is too late, there's nowhere to come back to. It's Guilt. When night tried to catch me I fought. Fighting for myself against the night, trying to find myself distracted me. We were well matched. Straightaway —never again. I did not fight. I fled. Into myself. When your body's on fire you are thrown into anguish as you jump out of the window. And there is no end to suffering.

'I'll be back.' No space left, just the abyss.

Despite my buzzing noises, a hand tears off my legs, a hand rips off my wings, the pain does not kill me, the body shrivels up; and outside the window there's no ground to lie crushed on.

And my two wings torn off.

I was running. I said to myself, it mustn't catch up with me. I know what it's going to tell me. I'd never seen it before. I won't see it as long as it doesn't catch up with me. It would be a dream. I had a thought inside me afraid to take shape. I was in a stifling endless sleep—the final reckoning was receding. I was moving on from one dream to another, or perhaps back—what reckoning?—If I woke up I would never know—it would still be open . . . and meanwhile I was being swept away by a strong current of feeling. Where can this apparently unknown thought be coming from, when my running away seems to show that I know it? I put my trust in my powerful mount. But the faster we went—how exciting— the more I felt the danger taking shape: I was certain that the thought was right there in front of us, and that it was, of course, nothing but Great Suffering.

It's just what I was afraid of. The worst. I was being carried faster and faster down the corridors of my dream, straight to it. I couldn't slow down and I didn't dare wake up; I was so afraid to know that what it was going to tell me would be true for ever.

I came across it on the bend. Impossible to stop it. It named the Worst for me: 'From those who have disappeared,' it told me. 'Never? Never?' I begged. I knew what it would tell me. 'Not for a minute?' No help for you.

One night, about three in the morning, He-who-loves-you phones. His voice wakes you up. You weren't asleep; you were hesitating. He tells you what stops you sleeping: 'I won't be coming. I haven't got a minute to spare.' He'll tell you tomorrow what he told you yesterday. You were expecting it. You're never prepared. It couldn't be a dream. It was too painful not to be only too true. Time can't spare you a minute. Love tells you: 'I can't spare you the minute I haven't got.' It is precisely your minute it hasn't got. That's why you couldn't come into being. How can you stop sleeping, dreaming, crying, chasing about in the night, since time had no time for you any more? The worst is that you know it couldn't be just a dream.

If the mother you love puts you down when you're about three years old, don't move, don't ask for anything. You won't get what you ask for. 'Wait for me.' Above all don't wait for her, she won't be back. Childhood is over. Now, wait! Crouch down on the cold tiles, huddle up, make yourself smaller and smaller—I'm great at reducing—shrink to the size of a small volume, hide your legs, make your buttocks, hips, all your flesh disappear inside the book; put your arms away, pull your head in sighing in horror; be quiet, save your life, give her, the one who has disappeared, an eternity (not) to come back. All those minutes and more. But I can't obey. Hell! a cry of Pain is growing inside me, taking root in my belly, its claws in my bladder: the book opens, phrases piss out, rats gnaw at page after page—gutted by anguish like a drawn chicken. If only this were a metaphor! But it's not just urine and faeces running out of the body, but all the organs of love.

A quarter of an hour: interminable. The period of the Great Suffering: from one minute to the next no bridge, no road, the body can't get through any more, your mind doesn't work any more; where time used to pass, a wall of years has been erected, years which are more and more impenetrable, pitiless, compulsory and blank. It is possible for a human being to get through them; it is impossible not to force yourself to climb over them, to penetrate them, to spend your whole life trying to master them, wear them out, put them down. And you crawl along, your head filled with barren boulders that stop you thinking. With no one to promise you that you will come to the end of the interminable.

I see myself writing a letter of Amazement: Letter to No one:

'Why did you choose me? I didn't come looking for you. You came after me. I ran away from you. The minute I saw your face I knew. I saw the end of my story and I fled. I ran away, threw myself into the floods in the street, buried myself in the sand; I did all I had to to save myself. Why did you catch up with me again? You ordered love for me, as if for a being apart. Why did you prescribe the absolute for me, if I must be imprisoned in the senseless moment, if I must be placed in the body that does not move, betrayed, a prisoner, my two eyes burnt out, my legs torn off—to please death.' I draw blood from the letter, seal it with my tears and excrement and send it in the three languages that I don't understand any more.

'*Why was my breeding ordered and prescribed, as of a person separate to God designed for great exploits, if I must die?*'

11

And I send the Letter: Being for No-one, to god herself.

'Why did you show me the beauty that causes death? You charmed me with your blood, you carried me when I could still walk, you held me up in your arms, your song made my soul ache with a sweet pain, you held me against your breast when I could still fly. Why did you give me the longing for the inner when I could still get out—if I must be nowhere?'

'For that very reason.'

You ask No-one your way: 'How do you get to Living?' Everyone knows. Everyone does what has to be done: Nothing. Be. Fooled. Don't think about it! Don't think about it!

Yesterday I had the Secret. And there was no secret.

Who's dumping me on a corner between times? Who's taking a hatchet, attacking me ferociously, my head, belly, the middle of my chest, without finishing me off? Who's making me suffer the scene of Great Suffering? How terrible! Life stops a few paces off and I see I'm not there any more. I thought I came from you!

The person in whom I was happily dreaming leaves me alone for a quarter of an hour between two worlds. While my mother wasn't there questions arose, cutting me to the quick. Where's mother? Answer! They questioned me to draw sense. Struck down. They stuck needles in my temples, in my stomach, answers in my head, where's mother? Where's the ground? Two iron fingers in the gullet to make me throw up love. Where do you think she's gone? Why do you trust her? Why did you desert her? Why didn't you write to me? Do you think she'll be back? She's vanished into thin air. What you love does not come back. Why ask her questions? The most dangerous questions. When will it end? Why did you close your eyes? Close the door? Open your eyes? What have you

12

done with your love? Where did you lose the Letter? Could you really believe you were unforgettable? Who gets the better of death? Who really believes death is fallible? She whom you trusted has chosen you in order to set you apart. You shouldn't have loved her. What you love is condemned. You've done all you could to kill her. Don't think about it any more! You'll end up forgetting her. Death told me that. I've seen her dead. Who killed her? It's your fault isn't it? You love (her) to death. It's love who wants to die.

They dragged me onto the stairs. Up! Up! By my arms, hair, ears; up such harsh steps; no question of stopping: they dragged me by reason which obeys its own laws and reaches its logical conclusion—madness. Trust! I do trust. Who's telling me not to trust?

I do trust. A quarter of an hour is endless. Meanwhile you lose your peace; innocence is burnt to ashes; you lose wars, you lose right and left, imagination, the shape you were born with. If there is room for you, you can't see it any more. In front and around you everything is dark. Darkness and fire, your bones are black and black veils shroud your heart. I think she could be dead; it would be stupid not to think so. Doesn't she have the time to die? No news since the last sentence. Why didn't you write to me? You said: wait for me. Why? Aren't I the one who is waiting for you? Perhaps I died over there. No news. Aren't we mortal? Why am I here? To believe just that.

I didn't die; I dragged myself along on my belly over the shattered ground; I ripped my belly, legs torn off, so lonely, dregs of the earth, no wings, back broken, a black worm, a torn-out tongue, the buzzing noises I made disgusted me. Why did you bring me up?

What is going on where I am is enough to make you howl in terror: eyelids cut off, I see everything, I see the invisible, in the dark I see the worst. Blindness is gone. I waited for her in

13

the dark. Her Letter didn't arrive. A path appeared, took hold of me, deported me, led me through my own entrails to a dead-end. Now I am outside and I no longer know how to get back. Waiting drove me out, swept my head away, drove me here, where there's no way out. The last door has closed behind me. I did not move, I didn't want to. You don't want to kill yourself. It's the world that's vanished.

I was crawling along in the dark—the questions caught up with me again. They hurled themselves on top of me and pierced me to the heart. No one to protect me. They struck at me without pity, pulled my entrails out of my belly, made me believe the unbelievable, nosed around in my flesh. They scattered the little sense I had left, it was all over my face, staining my mouth, my eyes, the stench in my nostrils. They gave me your news. Whose? They made me say everything that leads to death yet forbids it. And despite myself, I said: Who are you? Where is the Letter? Where is She-who-knows-Who-I-am? Call her. Louder. Softer. With feeling. Don't ask her to come. Haven't you got the name wrong? How could you have got it wrong? All the names you fling out, in all languages, are aimed at the same woman. And even without a name, aren't I the one who's calling her? What do you think of her silence? If you love her, don't think, don't start to think if you want to love her, don't call her. How can you not call her? If I don't call her, nothing is called anything, everything will disappear. The air will get thicker and thicker. Words won't be able to break through any more. A wall of ice will be built up. What then? She did write to me. The Letter got lost. The answer has been sent, it's just that I haven't received it. It's my fault. So she only wrote you once? No news is good news? You can't really believe that. Have you lodged a complaint? It's her fault. It's her right. Who says it is?

What was I up to while she was calling me? I only have one name, she must have forgotten it. The post isn't working. You can believe that the post has gone wrong. There are spirits everywhere. Death can do quite a lot you know. Are we

14

stronger? weaker? than the post? than death? Call me! Call me!

Call yourself! Wretch! Write her a long letter of reproach, in the name of all your suffering. To wipe out the separation. In whose name? She has all the names on her side. To avoid signing it. Sign: your nominee. Not to be sent. It would be returned to you. Isn't it already addressed to you? By No one? Who wrote the first line? Who carried on? Who can answer for me? She who doesn't answer me.

You were innocently pushing on ahead. With no thought of thinking. Not knowing what you knew. Mother's milk— Peace. Who puts us to the test? Who tries to upset us? Who condemns us to be schooled? The enemy took advantage when she-who-is-my-Answer left me alone. Each second jolts me from head to toe. Are you well rooted? The earth splits open—one more try—roots start to appear. Then time hits you harder and harder. You committed me to waiting. The moment you left, absence came back in: I was trembling, still holding out my arms to you; absence hurled itself in front of me, I couldn't duck, it flung its most dangerous question at me. Don't listen to it! It's a trap. No one can escape it. Things fell apart, words got twisted. When that question blows up in your face it wounds all living things. No more peace, never again, not for a minute. Space caves in. Time's a disease. The question asks *your* reason-for-being there. And *its* reason-for-being here is precisely to occur to you when you don't even have the strength left to invent a reason, nor to believe that there ever had been one before the Great Suffering. If there was one, you've lost the secret and can't even remember if there was one. Nor can you believe that there might be a reason later on, for while you were Suffering, when the past shattered, you lost the future too. Today, I had news of death, through my flesh. Death lets me know that His Cruel Majesty is at my service: 'No need to wait for me. I'm here. No one more trusty than I.' Don't believe death! If a little taste of

15

death comes into your mouth, spit it out. When there's a bitter taste on your tongue, don't swallow. There are some words that make you sick. Certain thoughts poison language. If the question arises, don't say anything. Even if you are wounded keep quiet. You have no reason-for-living? One always lives without reason. Run away! How? Don't listen. Don't ask where life is. Run!

I crawled along. I trust you. Aren't I crawling?

There never is a reason-for-living. Live for nothing; live for no one. If the reason occurs to you, run away, save your life.

While I was crawling along in the dark, I was struggling, hurrying along. I felt my guts laid bare, no hand to hold them in. I moved forward and found myself on the same spot; I wasn't discouraged, it wasn't a bad spot. But I couldn't stay there because I'd got there the wrong way; I couldn't find the way-out until I'd got there the right way. I was getting weaker, or the pain stronger, and there were more and more obstacles in my way. Don't turn round, thoughts closing in on your body—it's enough to drive you mad. What if I allowed the thought? The idea made me shudder and I lost my meagre advantage. Don't think! I wanted to shout: False! or Not true! or Leave me alone! or Get out! The very idea made me recoil. I fell down, I was turned over. I thought: 'This is it.' I was bound by my own entrails. Questions fell thick and fast. Is there a door to come back through? Who opened it to death? Questions poured down splitting open as they fell all over me. Are you sure? Sure? Who has faith? Do you? Didn't you come close to death? What are you waiting for? Are you sure you have faith? Have you really tested it? Who told you you had? Who's forgotten you here? We're here to test it. Who got you into such a state? Whom shall we Blame? Who will believe for me?

Do you believe? How strong the word 'believe' sounds when it's really an 'I-don't-believe!' How much faith have you then?—Beaten black and blue—Don't you believe? Who believes you? The less I believe the more I trust; the more I

16

trust the harder it gets. Who is inside me, siding with I-don't-believe, against me? Faith; broken faith. Forked tongue. Guilty.

Madness! I've lost my no-reason. You ask where is life? There's no answer. Who lost it? gave it? is it?

But no one can know until she's reached where it is *not*.

Before going out I understood, and quickly I let out my last cry. No one to hear me fall until the quarter of an hour is up. Outside you'd think there was nowhere to run to any more, and you'd be right. But there is still suffering and flesh to bear it. It's enough to make you howl and run—nowhere. No way. Not even a way to think, guess, suspect. You are dumped there like a piece of rubbish, like a lump of being, an idiotic crumb of the vanished earth. Faith buzzes in your ears, lashes you, falls on your back; it's no use trusting, praying, shouting, rolling on the spot, doubling up; even if you wanted to make something up, the imagination needs a little bit of possible world to work on, a tiny little bit of ground from which to attempt the most dangerous leap—but there isn't anything. You feel human life is near. Not for you. Eternity's stopping you from approaching it. A trifle, but insuperable. You feel life close by. The beings over there have ground under their feet. And I can't cross over. You have no introduction.

How easily you came into being before the accident, every morning, and sometimes several births a day! It can't be taught. It's not an art. Everyone who loves does it. Spontaneously. You love, you are loved, you are mother, you are born, you are born-mother, you are born-child.

What letter? Didn't get it. And what if he had written to you, signed: Your mother: he-who-loves-you. An evasion of doubt. Don't touch it; don't open it. If you receive it, take it. Tear it up. Haven't you read it before? Your whole life long. So you still think he could have not written? Don't know. Wasn't I put here for this: my flesh—a whole page of suffering? He wrote you the letter that destroys. That destroyed you. Skinned alive. Flayed. Don't read this letter: 'I ask you to love me as if I didn't exist.' Torn up. While you were writing, doubt appeared; who summoned it? I turned my face to the wall, I didn't listen to it. Not for a minute. Hadn't I already read? I turned to the wall, I didn't let doubt finish. It bit me several times, beginning on the nape of my neck. While it was wounding me, I received your letter. Without needing to read it I signed each word with my own meaning. Who wrote to you: 'Wait for me.' Who phoned you: '*Beloved*. Wait. Don't go away.' Who read you the decree? 'I'll be back in a second. Birth put off till tomorrow.' Tear it up—what madness! A second? Which second? The one that hasn't gone by yet? Will never go by. In the middle of the night, about three a.m. I pick up the phone. It's at times like this that you guess god's will. You say to yourself I'd better turn my face to the wall and go back to sleep. You turn to the wall. And he says: 'As if I didn't exist. Wait for me!' Who sent me that? Tucked up in bed, trusting. Betrayed, a prisoner, with my two eyes torn out. My enemies gaze at me. See through me. Why did you choose me? Promise? Carry me? Send me the telegram? 'I ask you to love me as if I were dead?' I told you: don't read. Are you sure? Absolutely. There are gods everywhere. Are we stronger than them? Pretend that the letter could have got lost? I can't. Wasn't I born in order to receive it? Prepared for passion, raised for sacrifices, nominated for the absolute—with two eyes so that they could be put out? As if you spent your whole life receiving the letter telling you the worst; send it back; turning your face to the wall—to weep. While it is being written and coming true.

Write this letter: 'I ask you to love yourself, as if I wasn't coming back,' obey. Do it for him. For he who asks the impossible of you. He is your mother and you are his little child. Be unmarried mother and child

Give birth to yourself! How I'd love to! No body here for me to live in. If you are outside the body where the blood flows, where the heart is struggling in the grasp of clutching hands, how do you get back to yourself? And all that was left of me was skin and bones. Fingers clutching at the heart as if they were clutching the breast, the wheel, the arms of your lover. Give birth to me! Pick up the pieces! Stick me together with your glue.

Grope your way to the border. Between heaven and earth. Bring yourself into being. Give birth to yourself. Be love's belly. The second mother. Love yourself for she who went away. Mother is here, mother is there, she's still here, there, and everywhere, wherever you want to give yourself a body going to and fro, hopefully, between the wall and death. Be your mother, have the child. Try it: a door will open. Don't ask anybody where to get it—Say all this to yourself.

It was 5 June 1937. Someone was being called. 'Well?' Scolding, the mother said: 'It'll soon be time'. So it wasn't a dream. Imagination had started working. 'Already!' I said. In mid labour. How could you doubt it? Imagination can only work when it has something perfectly sure to back it up. 'Already.' And as I said that word I began suddenly, slowly, in the deepest and most accessible level of myself, to unearth, to wake up, to get busy. Sadly. To doubt. And the scene? Impossible. To doubt. Can't you trust mother completely? Trust her calling? At least trust the ground under your feet? After all, this was a serious experiment in language: if you were being called there must be a bit of ground for you to be on. It's time! She was certain. So someone was going to come? Sometimes extraordinary things happen deep

19

down in your body, without your knowing. Time passes, being passes, sometimes people pass, letters which you wouldn't address to yourself if they had to be read; and answers to the next people to come in occur. While you weren't there. As if you had answered the call. Mother was preparing the first napkin, she folded it in a triangle, she was announcing me. So I was going to be born! Myself my mother, my child. Bashful. First I'd heard of it.

You see her moving about. You are welcome. You see yourself wrapped up in a large sheet of paper. Me, the stranger, the one who was expelled, being made such a fuss of! I hadn't thought of anything like that for such a long time. Things had been happening to me somewhere else—differently; where no one was speaking to me. Being born! You never forget. Once you've learnt how to be born, it's like learning to swim, birth stays for ever in your body, a potential seed, always ready to make itself felt. You get up, move forward, part the waters with your arms. My joy was braced against a fear which it was trying with all my might to nip in the bud. Why did you call me? I was asleep. She brings back reality. Betrayed! Re-called? You were dreaming you were going to live.

Yes, yes, it's not impossible to begin again. The game's not lost. Joy still had the upper hand.

What are you worrying about? What's making you look so drawn? What makes you want to turn over on the ground and run away? When your mother is calling you what makes you not want to hear your name; stop your ears and your mouth with earth? What makes you answer 'absent'? Why not say: 'Happy day, oh happy day!' Yes, yes. But it's my belly I'm worried about. Aren't you proud of your belly? It's flat, even a little hollow; it's a bit muddy. Because I've been crawling. It's even a bit torn. Who would think you are carrying yourself? Who would think you are going to end up giving birth to the new you? Your clean little body is going to come out. They'll congratulate you: What a big girl you are! You

20

created yourself while you were asleep. No fuss and bother! No magic wands and snakes! No pain, no pregnancy. No one to bother you with advice. You've got the knack—just like a woman—hey presto! You were always inspired—a natural. Give birth. Reproduce. Mother will take care of the formalities. One moment please! I examine myself. Look at your body. A barely perceptible curve. In the past the world was round. Houses had doors. Bodies came out into sun lit gardens, most of the time. When the curtain went up scenes were acted. There was plenty of room, plenty to see. You had a future. You wrote letters. And the letter came with no anguish to whoever wanted it. What's holding you back this morning? Don't think. Go on. Your belly is flat? Perhaps it has thought up another way of reproducing. The child is standing up in the lungs perhaps. That's a good explanation. All explanations are so good, so true! What's missing? Haven't you got what you need to shelter it: a little bit of flesh, a patch of ground, a triangle of fabric, a name so that it can live while you look for a place to be let in, where there'll be room for you? Wasn't there any sea where you fell? Couldn't we use the blue bath? You've lost almost everything but there is enough left to start all over again. You know very well you are waiting. Waiting? Oh yes! More, more! To be delivered? Ladies and Gentlemen, Fathers and Mothers, one moment please!

Nothing moving in my belly. I do so want to give birth, but I've forgotten how. Never mind that. It's a question of faith. Don't doubt. Believe. You count up to three, and at three you begin. You've got the belly and the love. Close your eyes and open your mouth and out pops the little child. One! Two! Mother says: One! Life says: Two! But when I wanted to say Three the word didn't come out. I couldn't say it. A voice seemed to be prompting me, but the word stuck in someone else's throat and the thing didn't happen. And yet I opened my mouth, but my tongue didn't move.

What didn't you do? What did you forget to do?

21

The birth-master is calling me. But it's not my name from before. I'm worried. I am woken up in the middle of the night. I was three years old. 'Get out. It's time.' I try. I take a step in the dark. The darkness quakes. I grope my way, the wall is spinning round. I climb up and up, it's so hard but I manage to take a step, the wall rises round me, everything spins round. And the way-out doesn't come. Somewhere else, it's time. 'It'll be time.' I was hurrying so fast. What time? She who knows how you are born didn't teach me how to come back in, to get out. It's guilt. I obey. I get up. I fall over, terrified. Time dies on me. Outside myself in no man's land, where no one arrives intact. Why announce my birth to me, once, twice, and no one the third time? While she wasn't there. As if I didn't exist. I was yelling, insulting her. She who wanted me has gone off. 'Why did you smile at me? Why the smile to provoke desire? I was lit by your smile. You promised me light. You rocked me. You sent me to sleep when I could still plan. Why did you give me a longing for daylight now that night is rising up around me, names are changing and I must come into being as if you didn't exist? Time didn't come back. I am in the land of no return. If there is a door, it's slipping away from me!

'Wait for me.' Time shatters. Trapped between two periods. Don't move. It'll pass. Will it be long now? A quarter of an hour. Nights began falling. I was waiting for the light. How many nights are there in a quarter of an hour? Fifteen or twenty, if you're a good girl. But in one night there is the whole story of death, and a disaster every second. It was a bad quarter of an hour. Deserted? Who packed you off here? God herself. I had just closed my eyes and she sends me off into the dead of night. And I don't know how to get through it. A hand! A hand! I was howling. No hand straightaway. Sleep only lasts a second. One short step and it's the end of the world. No one told me that. When a story is cut off, everything has to be begun all over again. Where you come

22

from is not where you are going to. I don't understand that. Who got you into this state? Guilt. She who put you down has gone off. That's unthinkable. In the dark I thought: it's not my fault. No light, no hand, no discoveries, no birth place. I didn't go looking for it, I came across it in the dark: a mocking thought which frightened me. It was much more certain than I was. Out of the blue, it hit me several times across the mouth. My tongue was bathed in blood, I was dribbling. If it weren't for the blood I would have said no.

No! she has not deserted me. Desertion arrived while she was out shopping. Don't open the door! Hide!

I wanted to run away. Before, there was a way out. No eyes. No doubt. With hesitation. I had made up my mind. Pretend you were at the door; the door opens, you step forward, you are saved! —But you are at the door, you must go through, it opens—that's obvious—and you can't go through. What's stopping you? Isn't there a door? Haven't you got legs? Aren't you awake? Didn't you make the decision? Exactly. I must get out of that door. It's a matter of life and death. I lift one foot, put out my arm, only to find that I am beside myself once again. Failed! You are doing it wrong. It's a question of orientation. I go back. The door is there. You think. You measure yourself. It is not impossible. Physically, and from the human point of view it is necessary.

There is a page. You struggle. I throw it onto its back. It is lying flat on its back. My left hand holds it down firmly. It doesn't move. It gives in. The right hand is raised. You aim. The pen is filled. You have all you need to get at it. All the lines are laid down. Where are you leading us? To the other side. You begin. You make up the first part. Then you come to the end. Full stop. You are skipping. No hesitating. Go on. Every morning it's the same old story: you struggle, overcome, stretch out the other, get through and writing turns its back on you. You are going to enrich the universe. You arrived this morning; the battle began, you won as usual, the sheet of paper was subdued, your right hand well equipped. You pounce, the line slips away, the page twists round. You straighten it, attack, beat it repeatedly, impose your will. But what you dictate can't be written down. Instead the page says: 'crap' and all sorts of obscenities. Under these circumstances you would give up, if you were wise. 'Don't be obstinate, it's a trap! Put it off till tomorrow.' But when you're seething with anger who listens to the voice of prudence? And if this voice speaks, isn't it just adding fuel to the fire? That quavering voice. Mischiefmaker. The voice of wisdom is deluding you, beware, just listen to your anger. Don't go on? Refusing to be put off, you dash, quivering, for another sheet—that's easy—there's hardly time to try and cheat, to try for an indirect attack. You pounce on it, the paper rolls over, you cling on, you are not going to be the one to let go; in the struggle you sink really low, as if you were fighting a mad boar. You wallow, dirty yourself. What is the point of stopping where you are now, bogged down, humiliated, dazed from the struggle? What is the point of going on? Who's forcing you to begin all over again?—ten pages, ten failures—who's leading you further and further astray, who's stopping your ears? Your hand is covered with blood, you are up to your eyes in mud, your pen has run out, someone has bitten you on the wrist, your left hand is paralysed, the right is burning . . . where are the worlds you thought you'd create? Your thoughts are turned to ashes and your breath is foul, your breasts and belly are ripped, as if the same sentence had been scratched onto you ten times over. Who wants your hide? Who wants to bring you to rack and ruin? The paper. And you yourself draft the decree: it is you who order your own execution. You accuse yourself, you are prejudiced against yourself. You make yourself guilty, your defence weakens. You are being pushed, brutalized. No one's against you being saved, no one's against your death. You could escape any time. But it all happens as if the paper had decided: 'You will not write.' And that is the order you have to write from this morning onwards, and carry through. Your torture: when the writing that you love, as you love yourself, rebels and spits out the sense you'd given it straight into your face. It's not to blame. What you anticipated has come about. Don't complain. It's your fault. What you feared is happening and it's not by chance either: your death was a page ahead. When death comes on the scene, you don't want to know, you ignore it; wasn't I born to overcome it? As if it were an illness: does it 'catch' you? But you will get better. The day is drawing to an end. Slaughter and desolation. All hope in ruins. You've no strength left to write. You've no longer the strength to get away from the scene where your monstrous abortions lie dying. You've no strength left to tear your body away from this scene of destruction. Anyway, you don't want to. You hate yourself. You loathe yourself. You haven't got the strength not to write. One last try. You let yourself be pushed, buried, beaten black and blue, you let yourself write. You know that all you can write now is mud, crap and rubbish. That's why you pick up a page, confess everything and sign, basely. To punish and assassinate yourself. Today you fought with all your might so that you would fail totally. And you've been beaten. You've won.

You want to talk about the anguish that leaves you speechless. The door opens. And everything stops. What's missing? A little air. A little time. A breathing space.

A calamity came looking for me. I've been fighting for so long. Without arms, without understanding, without imagination. Sorrow versus me, and my Strength-in-person won't come back. Someone was arguing. Careful! No arguing. The waiting-room is so cramped you hardly dare move. How could I fail to be tempted after so much anxiety, such a load of fears and failures, such loneliness, such a brutal quarter of an hour? Despite these three years—haven't you lived three years at least? Three years of uninterrupted enjoyment, submerged, stuffed, indulged, taking it easy, with my roots so firmly bedded. That's exactly it! You had time then. When I didn't know how to count. I just soaked them up. Timeless: endless bed, being in someone's arms, air all the time. Ways in—not doors. Time of mother's milk. You were in eternity. Peace time, no trouble, no delays. No explanation. Who stopped me from living on nothing but mother's milk—and now it's dark? And my strength is limited. I can't say it's mother. It's desertion.

When God gave you your strength, She slipped it to you in a smile, to show you what a fragile gift it was.

A calamity came. I let it in as if nothing had happened. I was in a hurry to talk it over. Time is so unstable: from five minutes ago three sad years. I was filled with hatred. Who hates? She who has a right to. 'Didn't I give you three years?'

Even the earth was restless, tossing in its bed, and there were hands in the air, groping around, trying to catch me, take me by the throat, hit me on the head. As for the ground where I was staggering about, there was hardly any left; my 'reception' room was a faint outline. It had a wall to lean against, but I couldn't bear it because, as soon as I brushed against it, millions of ants swarmed over my arms. I didn't mind that; the place was irrelevant. It was all in my head—and Waiting was driving me mad.

It was January 26th. What is there in this quarter of an hour? How much time? How many Stories? How many successful assassination attempts? How many avoided? You don't arrive, you are suddenly let loose in the Land of Terrors. And from one minute to the next there is no time: between each minute, now curtains of lead, now corridors of fire. You'll get

26

through. No sun. The sky has caved in. The air presses like a giant knee on your chest. And you are crushed. You aren't living. You are dying. Endlessly. The head can't bear it any more. You don't really know who has to die. Whether it's good or bad. It is a question of someone dying. Who could say to herself 'It can only be you'? Who could think 'It can only be me. It's you, then'? It's a question of love. No one to ask the question. It's a question of good luck, which comes and goes in the waiting-room, as if seeking a heart. A question of bad luck. What does it want? To record its pound of flesh. It pauses for the moment; it doesn't know who would answer it. It's a question of hearing. It can happen that you don't hear it, or that you don't quite understand who it wants. Because it is calling from far away. Who are you asking for? One of you. No one in particular. Who gave our address? Who gave our name? Neither of us has provoked it. The air between us vibrated. I didn't even open my mouth. How could it know who to talk to? Don't our bodies change their names depending on the time, the need, the anxiety? Depending on the questions? Depending on whether it's a matter of life or death, going out, coming back, or not getting in? Whether it's a question of receiving the threatening letter? being there to receive it? tearing it up without reading it? Not reading it, as if it wasn't addressed to you; to me; as if you'd read it before, torn it up before; as if I had written it, or one of us; not to be sent; but to torture yourself in advance; in order to give death who longs for us its little reward; stave off its hunger; as if you'd left the letter lying around, to forget it; to send it off, absent-mindedly; in order to bring off a gesture that had misfired; so that the threat is received; by one of us; so that one of us is hurt for the other—in the name of love.

There's a fault trying to get itself recognized. Why me? I get rid of it. It's not my fault. It was hanging around. It was nearly the end of the month. My body was trembling with weariness. Why should I accept the blame? I don't think it was my fault. Someone phoned me. It wasn't you. I pick up

27

the phone—and there it was. Don't answer. It won't be him. I answered. It'll be Guilt. It was. In the end you no longer know why you answer, who you wish to speak to. Who could say if anyone is free from guilt? It is a question of endurance. Seduction. Lack of experience. Necessity. When you are besieged why do you give in? The enemy wants death. He reminds you every morning, until you want it too. It isn't that you've been conquered. You aren't giving in to threats, you aren't at the end of your tether, you still have provisions left. You could hold out to the end. You are not under a delusion: you don't take the enemy for you mother. It isn't that you like death. It's that you want to punish life.

Who can know who 'I' am when I am dying? When you give in to death, you don't know who 'I' will be.

I held out for so long. But it was January 26th. I'd lost too much sense. Things were confused. Guilt had me summoned. I was so afraid to fail. It's not my fault. It's so dark. I can't see a thing. When mother goes out you should beware. Shut yourself up, barricade yourself in. Impossible. When you go out, the door opens and absence comes in. Death announces itself. It's not me who wants to open the door. Your absence stops me refusing. Advises me to answer. What should I do? I am hurting us. You don't have to answer, but you are forced to because you are Waiting.

When an invitation to suffering comes to your address, how can you not accept it? Not refuse it? If it's in the name of love? That depends on the name of love.

Doesn't love change its name depending on whether I am calling it, or you? Depending on how long you've been waiting, depending on how urgent and painful it is? Depending on how strongly you wish to hate, where the hate comes from, where it's going to? Depending on the cause? Depending on what is left for us to desire. Depending on the body that isn't there, when you are not there, if my body is missing it can only be with you, if absence answers for us.

When it's a matter of my body, there is a mother; there is a child. Who am I? She-who-doesn't-know-who-is-dying. Where does the invitation come from? One of us must have sent it by mistake, as a precaution. It can't be me, and so it's not her. No one is to blame, except Guilt.

Someone must have been afraid that she wouldn't be seen dying.

My punishment, my pain, my love, my fault! I saw myself sitting in your place beside the bed in which your child was lying, he was dead, you were my mother, sitting crying beside the bed, I was your child and your pain hurt me.

Until you have come close to death you cannot say how many 'I's you are.

In a dream you see yourself receiving the last letter and you weep: 'Life will be short.' I was in despair. I was writing to you: 'Life *was* short. It's no longer up to me.' I sent us death messages and reading them you wept.

While she isn't there, he turns his face to the wall; he is dying. Face to the wall, watching yourself die, from the beginning. Seeing all the deaths, all my fatal clinches, all the deaths that have pursued me, caught up with me, flung me to the ground, have fallen upon me and embraced me. Deaths that have hit me hard with one hand and caressed me with the other. I have struggled, knocked them down, succeeded in getting up again, managed to start my life all over again, in order to be She-who-is-waiting-for-you—but I've never forgotten them.

He told me: 'I'll be back between the 15th and the 20th.' I believe you. You are the one I trust. It isn't him I mistrust. It's space. I fear the hatred of things.

According to the child, guilt arose in a moment of

distraction. Always the same old trick: guilt has the power to force us into complicity with it.

It was late. You are taken by surprise more easily at night. The last minute of the day you remember that the worst is upon you. The End. You were probably so anxious not to see it that you've put yourself in the dangerous position where, because you wanted to avoid thinking about it, you are suddenly faced with it in reality and are now defenceless against it. 'Too late!' It's coming. Anyhow, who could have stopped this being but death? Even with our enemies we cling to idiotic habits of politeness: that's why, with death in my soul (his death, of course) I feel bound to go and meet it at the door. If we don't run away it is because, when the end is drawing near, imagination deserts us. We go to meet death, bring it back and cannot imagine the consequence. If only we had a day, an evening, just an hour left. But the letter says: 'Too late.' At times like this your movements are so heavy that when you dress it's as if you were putting on armour. But there won't be a war. It's peace-time already. You are beaten. Anyway, life is so short. One more or less.

What were you doing when you were living? I was reading *Tristan and Yseult*. I paused a minute. How did death come? It must have something to do with your reading. As if death had been summoned through my body—and the absence of yours—by a few lines in a book. As if death had wished to appease my deepest anguish. Of course it must have taken advantage of the spaces between the lines. While I was reading *Tristan and Yseult*, living it, longing to see death arrive, too late, longing to calm the sea, keep him alive one more night, an hour, only a minute, a minute which would go on for another three days, just enough time for her to come and watch me dying, a message arrived: 'He won't live long. You failed to come to his aid. It's no longer up to him.' My eyes were full of tears, the walls were vibrating with my pain, even the earth trembled. It was my fault. He had said: 'Twenty days.' You ought not to have read the Story of Death. There are ways of running away from suffering that lead us straight to it. Could I have escaped? I wasn't running away, I was being carried away. Because I had to Wait I was compelled to read the book which forces you to give in to the worst: the story that gives death as the final consolation. You were reading aloud, as if the calamity had already happened. I let it in. I was impatient to get it over with. The three years were over. And it was the twentieth day. Even the earth was exhausted; nerves were on edge, air couldn't circulate. When you feel that the earth can't go on any longer; the birth of each new second is accompanied by such convulsions, the next will be the last; the sky is at its last gasp; such pain in the burnt-out, distended lungs; trees twisted, roots turned over; finger-nails torn out, fingers turned to ice try to shatter the chest, to crush the heart, but the skin is as tough as iron—how could you sleep?

Time drips so slowly through the veins in your brain and it's this slowness that fills your soul with a craving for slaughter. You must have movement, killing, the blood must be freed. Axes, lightning steel, huge butchers' knives come into your head. Take hold of your scythe, it fits your hand like a glove. I see myself moving forward, I see its rhythmic swing. Straight after the first slash of the blade you feel a change for the better; what a relief, walking, striking—forests, mountains, piles of flesh—axes come so naturally to you, you're in your element; they sink into bellies like a knife into butter—that's death's power. You'll wait to think about it later. Because, all you have to do for the time being is escape from this prisoner's body in which you were suffocating. And, for the moment, to start to think about anything but making good use of the scythe would be suicide. But there is nothing to be afraid of. I trusted to the tool's rhythm, my soul conquered by its clarity. You are gradually heartened, strengthened by the perfect movement so that you slip into the handle, you are taken over by the rhythmic swing and, joyfully, you become one with the cutting edge of the blade itself, whose rocking movement

31

renews in your flesh the dances which had ceased. It's the unhoped for slaughter, step by step, hacking my way through with renewed calm. Your arms fell and haunches were sliced off, rounds of leg, thighs, pieces of shoulder, heads fell—as space was cleared at last, blood began flowing again. You have a chance to be saved? Take it. You'll pay dearly but you don't have the choice. You must save what you can. It will cost you one of your lives, maybe both. I didn't know which. If it's you, is it me? I'll know by the pain. It was the last minute. I grab hold of the axe, pounce. Strike. The calamity was there, already covered with blood. 'Say what you have to say to me,' (I burst out.) 'I know it already. Out with it.' What suffering?

It doesn't depend on you but on the body you'd prefer to die in, at that moment. How difficult it is to know who to sacrifice, and then whom to be revenged on, to appease love's love of justice! Luckily, in such drastic cases he-who-is-loved appears with the speed and power of a banished god. I was on the last line but one: 'It's no longer up to me.' My eyes were full of tears, I couldn't breathe, impossible to produce another word: 'Finish it,' I said, holding the book out to Guilt. 'Hurry up. I know, but I can't write it down.' Guilt hardly has time to raise a hand before a door in the wall opens and the wrathful god returns! My memory dies on me. The book falls. Suddenly the scene catches fire. I rushed towards Guilt: 'Go away,' I said, 'get out, that way.' I would have done anything for Guilt to disappear before he saw it.

Anything? Yes. Would you steal? Yes. Kill? Yes. Yes. Burn, lie, murder, disown my father and mother, betray my friends, hand over my people to the enemy, commit unforgettable crimes—everything that is forbidden. Plus what no woman, sister, mother would do? I would do the impossible too. What about your children? Desert them? Stab them in the back, the heart, cut their throats? My son too, with his eyes on me—light of my life—I would put out each eye, my eyes on him, watching me, I would see him blinded, even he, and he

32

wouldn't die, I wouldn't kill him, and I'd survive not killing him, his eyes put out, I would contemplate my night, without forgetting how he would look at himself in my eyes, with his lips on mine. From son to son, from generation to generation, cut off the light and hurl his descendants into the abyss. And your daughter? My daughter too. I would do what I had to do so she could never again say my name. Let there be horror! And there would be horror. I would be the woman capable of thinking she could carry out such atrocities if necessary; she who would stand by and watch herself doing everything she can only be forced to imagine when she is threatened by an infintely more cruel punishment. I could imagine myself turning into that woman. Better not think about it. Swear. Humanity would cease. The children of this earth would be tucked up in bed in sheets of fire. Promise. Later. Sign: anything. With my eyes shut.

Who could accuse me? It's not me, just my name. It can't be you.

Who wouldn't be released from all human names if she were suffering such torment? Who wouldn't devour her children's balls, her father's eyes, the fingers on her own hands? Everyone would sign. Except the one you love. The cause: the mother for whom you sleep with death. To spite mother. You'd come to this! When you get that far, all the selves you might have been are destroyed. Unborn, yet already massacred. Your flesh crammed full, as if your body was their tomb.

I would have signed. This isn't my name. It's the name I am giving death. To deceive it. To make it wait patiently. Wait a minute. Afterwards, it won't be me any more. Take me. Torture me as I would like to caress the one in whom I wish to die, decay and rot. But do it discretely. This evening. Later. Without him knowing. The last minute will be such a short one.

Will you disgrace the one who is your mother and your father?

I would. I shall.

For love. Of whom?

To prevent him from recognizing the Guilt. So that he doesn't know. To spare him. So that he needn't be upset. Because of me. So he needn't get angry; needn't see himself forced to judge his creature, without being able to undo what has already been done. To spare him the pain of condemning her; of seeing her condemned; put to death; to spare him the pain of seeing himself condemned to send her away; lose her; pay for *me* with *his* soul. Because of Guilt.

In order not to watch him suffer and be the cause! The body is on fire, you jump out of the window. For love. So that my corpse is less terrible to look at. So at least you would not be disgusted, if I died.

My memory opens up. What terror! All the faces you detested, women you have ceased to be for such a long time now. An invasion. Escape. Fight. In the free-for-all you would kill yourself at random. Madness pounces on me: are they the old selves you hadn't succeeded in killing?

'Go away,' I said. I could have killed Guilt. No time. 'Get out, that way. I'll call you.' I pushed it aside. Later. I would have pleaded with it. I would have given anything. Thou shalt not commit adultery. I would have committed adultery, if only the guilt would go away. I would have promised. Haven't you already killed? lied? stolen? let in Guilt-in-person? Not to *his* knowledge.

I rushed to the door, kissed him, pushed him aside like a mother who gives her child a violent shove, to stop him being run over; pushed him into a corner so that he couldn't see it when the door opened. Then I came back to Guilt, tugged at it, threw it out. 'When?' it said. 'This evening,' I said. 'I see, still the same old farce,' it said. And Guilt—still the same old poison. 'When?' 'Later.' Idiot! Still the same old mistake. You lose your head. You don't know what you're doing any more. And crimes are committed. 'I'll be back.'

At last, in the room with him, a breathing space, and all the love in the world. But it will die. Alone, in front of the one for whom you have done your worst. Oh such sweetness flowing for ever, floods of tenderness, of desire, of sorrow, blood everywhere, and in the breast all the sadness and anger in the world. Wasn't there the book? As if he couldn't read! Wasn't the writing on the walls? As if he hadn't received all the letters I'd committed against him. Even though I hadn't sent them. At the last minute.

'My love, I have forgotten everything. My memory's seized up. I no longer know how to be born. No one can sign that.'

You lose your head. Always the same old accident. And yet it isn't the first time; but in this kind of affair experience doesn't count. Things have such a sudden, arbitrary way of recurring that you are never prepared. And yet you swore you would be the most suspicious, mistrustful, careful person in the world. You were not born to hold out in a siege, but you have transformed your whole life to be prepared for the worst. You never sleep. You watch over your frontiers continuously. You were fragile, easily taken in, credulous, dangerously unfit to judge the world. You idealized others, couldn't stop yourself from projecting an image of purity onto each one and you thought you lived surrounded by pure generous souls. Aren't we born for other births? You approached others without seeing them, you came closer and closer to caress their cheeks, their hair—as if lion-dragons, hyenas, the heinous were born of woman. And if they didn't listen to you, you supplied question and answer. And if they told you the truth: we were born to kill, you didn't hear. If you heard, you said, but haven't we come to change all that? The mediocre were right and you were wrong: you've fallen ten times into their hands and now you will not let yourself be betrayed, wounded, bitten to the bone any more. You arm yourself, give yourself instructions, examine, are well protected—if you are attacked by the mediocre you know how to deal with it. But the world is a big place, it may never happen again.

Anyway, things aren't the same any more. Aren't you armed to the teeth, forewarned, sharp witted, capable of cruelty. Now you can open up, go out, begin again, forget the past, go forward without worrying, approach people more freely, more confidently, more lovingly. You can let yourself be carried away, much farther, much faster than before. You can look forward to the beauty awaiting you, the generosities of soul you can allow yourself. You go through your little fortified domain happy, with a light heart, a new point of view, you turn the corner and run. To your ruin. And it has happened again: you fall into the clutches of the mediocre. So, the more you are armed the more easily you are disarmed. It is as if, in all this business, you had a somewhat crazy end in view, which you would have to deny, because it seems to mean this: 'haven't I done all I could so that no one could blame me for being responsible for the unhappiness that I am secretly, shamefully courting; hoping it will catch up with me, wound me to the quick like lightning, and prove conclusively the power of the mediocre, so providing me with the reasons I need for withdrawing from the world, and more cleverly still, give me all the reasons I need for letting myself be condemned by others to lose my head.' But the truth is that you shut your eyes to mediocrity, because it is all around you, and if you saw it, it would stop you wanting to go on.

That is why, when the enemy arrives, always where I am least expecting him, I lose my head. There is a chance to escape and then a scene takes place on the following lines: the last plane is about to take off. You've just got time to catch it. All you need is your mother, whom you are relying on, to drive you to the airport. Every minute counts: twenty left. Just enough to get out the car, start it, drive quickly to the plane, catch it 'on the wing'—saved. One minute later and you'd be destroyed.

In your mind everything is perfect: luck is on your side, so is mother, time, plane, necessity, boarding card. In reality, where is the car? Mother, sitting opposite you, is looking furtively at you and hasn't moved. And a quarter of an hour has gone by. Who could imagine that mother would let you down? Hand you over to the enemy? And now they are going to take you, tie you up, put out your eyes and jeer at your blindness. In a flash you see. I see everything. What I was, what I am going to be, and what I am now: a hive swarming with thoughts of death. And opposite me, she who should have supported me. You can run around the streets shouting for help, waste your strength looking for a taxi, refuse the final reckoning, as long as there is life left in you. But the world knows no pity; the taxis are taken, you've only got three minutes left which you spend abusing the mother who didn't bend over backwards to help you.

I scream: 'You're doing it on purpose, on purpose!' and each word is such a sharp knife that as you attack her with all your strength I cut my own tongue, which is dripping with blood. As if it were mother's fault. You would end up believing it was, if it weren't for the chorus of aunts and grand-mothers in the room where I'm dying, reminding me that I myself said to my mother: 'No need to hurry. I've got plenty of time. I'll make it.' When it's a question of destroying yourself you are not the only one to decide. Still the same old farce, and no one is spared. Everyone is wrong. Is wronged. You have to have made all the mistakes you had tried not to make, before you can say without being wrong: it's not my fault. It's not your fault. To mortify love as it seems to deserve to be mortified, to vindicate the ways of death. Apparently.

'My love, my love, how short life was.' I was writing that. It was signed: 'Your fault.' And if I died I wanted to have written: 'My pain, I am Your Majesty, The Child of Death.'

You wouldn't have sent them for anything in the world to the one you love. But he receives them just the same.

While you are making me wait, death watches over me. Sitting by the bed, facing the child to whom it tells stories which make him cry, as if he believed them. In his turn the child tells death even sadder stories. As if they could happen. I made them up.

I don't know if the man I love is my mother because I come into being for him, or because he is the one I don't want to die without. All my deaths are his fruits, I want him to enjoy them, that's why he is my mother. The cause of my hunger. His body tempts me, is necessary to me; houses me, shelters me, nourishes me. His smile makes me want to cry out, come running, lose myself, put my head between his teeth, hurl myself at his breast and, once the terror is passed, the threshold crossed, stride deeper and deeper into my world. The man with the smile is my mother in whom I have to live: make my bed in his chest, sleep face down under his lungs, wash my face in his blood, eat the tongue in his mouth; be eaten, my bones crunched between his teeth, become pulp, juice, flesh of his flesh, where I long to feel myself dying over and over again.

Not to be woken up yet.

I long to be with him as if nothing had happened, to rest just for a minute! Not to hear him say sadly to me: 'And so, I'll never have a family? No wife, no child?' Ah! Such pain! I leant my head against his chest. 'Isn't my whole life yours?' I said. My body sunk in unhappiness. He didn't deny it. I long to have lost my memory; to forget the appointment. To be everything to him, his wife, his child, his fault, his pain, eye for his eye—and my death to punish him.

And who will you be tonight? Better not think about it. It was all so dark. 'Why don't you help me?' I cried out. As if the fear of being alone with Guilt tonight had at last prompted an argument. 'After all,' I said, as I buried myself in his vast chest, 'Why don't you help me? Couldn't you chase it away?

Haven't I given you my whole life?' And my head plunged into a river of love, my arms parted the trappings of sorrow along its banks. Despite everything, I swam in his body as I longed to. He said to me: 'Why did you sign?' But his answer didn't reach me, I was already far away, where pain couldn't touch me. While the dream lasted. The crossing. One second before starting all over again.

'Between the 15th and the 20th.' Yes. 'I'll be back. That's certain.' Yes. What is 'certain'? Thinking about it, I don't know what the word means. Things change after the 20th. Night of disaster: take me, hold me, I don't know what to rely on any more; the 20th goes by, afterwards doesn't come, I am outside time! I can't live in the abyss. I am spewed up, night won't have me, the day turns its back on me. I am in the depths of infinite sorrow with no net, no meshes, all my fish tangled, my flesh can't even drown, I must suffer. I am at the bottom, in the temporary which seems permanent. I dream of 'up there', but it is a height stripped of all its glories, bleak, drifting, where people live and have no history and I catch a brief glimpse of a life I have no part in. Apart, you get up, go to sleep, not in a bed but in infinite sorrow which you can't shake off because it has become your second body. It is made up of huge quantities of pure absence: everything that didn't happen, won't happen, that has no name, no face; and all the names that have died, the words that are going to die, that you can no longer bring back to life. In that solitude, not like the solitude of the desert, but a loneliness that keeps you outside and beside yourself, in the place that you should be there is a hellish resignation. Yesterday I could think, name things. Coming back the 15th: I knew that anguish wouldn't have time to spring up. Between the 15th and the 20th how many adulteries? murders, moments of paralysis, rapes. But I couldn't count any more. They were not ordinary days. They had attacked me before, during the scene of the Great Suffering. Made a tomb of my body.

It's his fault. No strength to get up. Get me up! The man I

want to implore isn't listening. The one I want to accuse. In your arms; get me out of here; don't you see I'm dying? I'm frozen stiff. This death is not death.

The 15th gives me a shove, I staggered but I didn't fall over; there are the in-between days to get through. From the 15th to the 20th as slowly as possible, crawling along, to give him ten years; sleeping, not moving, to give him all the time he needs. Not to come. Until he does not come. This sickness is not fatal. You have to know how to make it last. If he didn't come, it's not I who would be destroyed, it's the world that would be without mercy, already sick, diseased.

It wouldn't be true to say I am completely alone. On the 20th I am with myself and the ghost of myself, thinking I am Almost-Not-Me any more. Me-Minus-Me that's something— 'minus' hurts but it isn't death. Don't blame yourself. Have mercy. Have pity on myself: put pity between me and Me-Minus—poor dumb brutes. When you pass the mirror you see yourself burning, here icy cold, there burning hot, with a fire that doesn't burn you, that used to burn you. Your face isn't even there any more. Someone is sorry for you. Why? Patience, misery: they are better than nothing. 'Up there' is no better: the whole of life spent huddled under the hull of a boat facing the desert of heaven.

Things that have begun badly, worse and worse . . . Give him time to postpone. Open up the wound a little wider so that living gets harder and harder. I receive the letter that does it: 'Leaving the 21st, or 22nd. Possibly the 23rd' and I sign it—do what you like. Either the 23rd or another day, in any case, there are so many days and no one to make them go by. The 20th comes, he doesn't come. Who will vanquish these vain days for me; afterwards doesn't come; every second it is the same day beginning all over again—I can see it, I'm not mad, time is making me sick. The letter said: 'leaving—20 —day of plenty—day of vanity, or the 23rd,' but Monday or Tuesday at the latest. Sentence has been passed on me, I read: 'Get up, go forward into the darkness, like a woman you are

40

going to die, like a child you will fall down, but Monday or Tuesday at the latest.' How I trust you, my love, I open my mouth wide to say it, and feed on thin air. Every day dawns without the sun. But Tuesday at the latest. Soon my head on his chest, between his breasts, my face between Monday and Tuesday, my mouth open and my tongue resting on Monday and Tuesday. I am the one who is fated to trust you. Immediately I say to Me-Minus: 'Be careful, don't be rash, give the greatest possible leeway to the one you trust. He said Monday or Tuesday, but who can say what days can intervene, what nights to hold them up? I stick the letter against my skin between my two breasts, bind your words on my brow; smooth me, wipe me, my tissue is covered in shit and I dare not even touch myself. I know it's not really true, but my feeling is stronger, I lie down, no one lifts me up; I want to wash but no one but you can touch me. I must escape, find the chink in the earth's wall, risk creeping in, outside there is another planet. I am told it is too cold there for human beings—never mind—you chance it—here in this camp there's no love. One more day and I won't be able to calm down any more, I'll fall into the arms of madness, and mad, I'll be nothing but a beast tearing its guts out, devouring its own entrails. Take advantage of a moment of carelessness, take the corner in one bound, get out of the earth with nothing on but dirt, mud up to your lips. At least you'll be outside where it is so cold that you might be forced to give in, but not straightaway—Monday or Tuesday at the earliest. And meanwhile you'll see troops of warm children leaping about on the hillsides. Wash your hair ten times in snow-soap which freezes your face, your thoughts, but makes your head whizz. I try, break down before I begin—I'll try again.

You wrote the letter stuck to my skin, so it is my life's blood repeating: 'You'll be two or three days without news,' joy and peace! Everything is so clear: first night, then day, how good the hunger feels between your breasts! I even like the word 'without', because I believe everything he writes. Two or three, four already. Perhaps six. Possibly Saturday? Very possible. Monday for certain. It could be any day. I had primed myself: let two be three. And it was so. Why can't you really feel that two is six? When you try to believe it, I shy away, lash out, kick out all over the place: the horse won't take the jump, his legs are rooted to the spot, no good sticking spurs into his belly, blood spouts, I scream and shout but I can't budge an inch. At the earliest has turned into at the latest. Not only not the 15th or 16th, not the 17th, not the 18th, not the 19th, not the 20th. I have the eyes of a woman but I am not a woman—I am Mad. I am she whom I feared, a weak, anxious animal; intractable, hypersensitive, one of those intelligent beasts who is always at risk, a horse's haunches, a hack's neck. The world of human beings is civilised, calm and deeply concerned with manifestations of culture; words circulate one after another, are received, like elegant cakes on a plate—I have no hands to take them, I have to balance my feverish head, I must not open my mouth, I would howl, my whole soul at the window of the world, in the void where I lie in wait for him to appear.

What if he doesn't arrive? It's no longer up to me, the limit has already been passed, my heart, my body would burst and splinters of pain would ravage the scene and force everyone to wake me up quickly, too late, or disappear.

I hold out my hand. Take my hand. Even the universe feels the danger. If my body exploded, you would perish too.

Not before the 20th at the earliest. And then, not in the new chunk at the earliest. The latest. Unless another new chunk begins. Two to three days don't bother you, six days at the worst, two or ten.

The body is placed on its belly, face down on a bread board, while the saw goes back and forth, starting at the ankles. You can bear it because of the rhythm: regular chunks, all the same length.

42

If he comes back: my hand in his hand, running together—let pain stay put in the earth—the two halves of my life united at last. You are no longer on the other side of the abyss that you opened up for yourself. All is supple, fast, positive, how simply and quickly everything happens when *he* is *me* is *us*—*we* are saved—before the universe blows up. I am totally trusting, I expect his hand at any moment, sure that at the latest will be at the earliest; it's just a matter of time—trust is hope. If it depends on hope, then my hand plunges into the dark; if it's not today, it will certainly be tomorrow and hope turns hopeless. My hand has been cut off, it is so naked, detached from the hand which binds it to the human body. In the night it bleeds, bangs against walls. At times too it touches me, finds my face buried in sheets covered in spittle and vomit. It feels my cheeks, eyelids, touches my temples, bird-hops onto my shoulders, my neck; is a tongue between my breasts. The hand reminds you that love once loved you: you had a body that didn't decay, ears of hewn stone, marble cheek bones, all your material solid, light like steel lace, indestructible skin—I was beautiful, I was created, a new model every day and never the same one twice. Touch me, touch me up, repair me with your fingers on my broken body. The stones of my body are not dead, my rags are not insensible, if I look like a dead jackal, do something for me with your fingers: my thighs have forgotten nothing, the hand may enter and flit with its bird-fingers among my rocks—don't run away from my excrement, settle below, walk among my bones, caress them, make my nerves sing out, my harp used to obey your touch. The hand finds my lips buried in mouldering sheets and my cunt full of ashes and torn up letters—my secret waste bin. This mouth is not dead, it just needs your merciful fingers to clear it up, the hand works fast, cleans me up. My hand is your hand, but sometimes I don't trust it; my body is so hopeless that happiness can no longer touch it. I wouldn't trust your hand

43

any more, sex no longer works, all that is left is my nerves vibrating with resentment. All that is left here is the breed of the jackal; if it were your hand I'd pounce on it, bite it and listen to the bones cracking, shuddering with a jackal's pleasure. Everything wears out. You change. And there is no compensation for so much anguish.

When things have begun badly you fall ill, the body decays, who would expect to see a woman when the flesh is rotten—even the bed has gone mad and the sheets spew out floods of ants. But it isn't your hand. It is mine writing: 'Impossible to resist. I wasn't the one who wanted it. Two has turned into eight. Signed: Your hopeless jackal.'

Not Monday, not Tuesday, another day, or another—plunge a knife into your throat, to let out the cry that is stopping you breathing. You can't say to him: 'My master, I owe you Nothing. You have given me back my old longing to die. All is lost, nothing is lost, life can go on, how alone I am, I am not myself any more.' I long to say that to him because it is true. But as soon as I turn to this man he is my mother smiling; what was true is false, the mouth opens, it's the abyss into which I fall into a dead sleep, while I wait for him to come back. Forgive her, it's not I who am deserting you it's that old indulgence: Madness—in a time of stress. The slut has vomited again: 'You have brought me back to the same point: where no questions are asked, where nothing is holding me back, I am held by nothing, life is hovering on my lips like a smile, I can watch myself dying.' With the eyes of a woman, even though I have ceased to be one. Like a dog returning to its own vomit.

In a corner, to get back to yourself, make up your face again. As if I were coming back, in my own eyes. Paint in bold strokes, in shades of ruby red, purple, dark blue huge, striking, brightly coloured eyebrows, so that the eyes return to their place, to look at me. Impose my old face, the one I had before I went out. What a good mask to charm myself. Enthrall my woman's eyes and appease them. Answer madness with the following telegram: 'Life doesn't depend on you any more. I like myself. Free. You don't have to come. All is well. Come.' Go back home, firstly, put a good face on things, hold up your head, despite opposition from the authorities; be loved, roused, carried away by your own will. What does self-love depend on? The dress you clothe your soul in. If you wore one you would be seduced.

Charm yourself, delight in your own inner riches.

To stop you looking outside and plunging into the theatre of terrors. To stop you seeing that the world is a disease, teaming in fancy-dress: its shops full of falsehood, with millions of machines who keep running to avoid thinking that they are working for nothing, to stop them seeing how full is the Void. All hands lead to Death. We have torn out Life's two eyes and now Death watches it writhing in pain, till the end.

Just in case, go on living, for nothing. Live because you aren't dead. Life has become so feeble that even sickness is losing its strength. Everyone lives: everyone has the secret. Everyone is dead but no one knows it but me. They are saved. Tongues talk. They are mad, but they don't know it. I am Madness, and I am alone. I was betrayed by trust. You trusted. You had the strength. You had a wardrobe full of dresses. You said everything that began with 'I.' You too were miraculously saved. Well-dressed, whole, cheerful. Streets led somewhere. Your feet carried you along. You ate all sorts of food that was good for you. Your eyes were well hidden. You didn't think of vomiting. Your flesh held together. Ideas came and went, discussed together, excited you, moved around, were dismissed, worked, were sorted out, vanished and reappeared, broke up, regrouped and there was always at least one that you liked and chose to love. You married ideas. From marriage to marriage sense perpetuated.

Neither rich nor poor. Evicted. With no dress, no light, no

45

eyes to rekindle me. I am my own widow. I am my own mother, cleaned out. Widow—vomited up. How cold and dark it is inside you! I lost myself, I used to live with myself, I used to wait. Within me were all the selves I would become: all my children, my inexhaustible future riches. I followed one scent, looked at your mouth only. And now, banished. God herself doesn't know why. There was an accident of faith. No rights or wrongs about it. Something snapped in my head. A trifle. A mistaken impression. The letter was so fragile. When I wanted to write: 'I like myself,'the tissue paper tore. The lines shied away. It's the anguish. Sense leaks out to the last drop. The tongue in my mouth speaks at random; what I mean to say is blocked. I would so like to speak the names that recall life, confirm it, swear to love it. 'You can be certain.' What is 'certain'? Who assures him that I love him? Who can be sure of me? When I want to swear love my tongue rebels and the words fall into the shit. It must have been frightened by a vision. Three days with no news, the next day catches fire, the flesh was too dry, when that's the case a nasty breath of air, the ghost of a thought, bring on disaster. Three senseless days, words burst apart, beasts flee from each other, horses go mad and devour each other. No more phrases. No one can be sure any more—except that he's not sure of anything. The split was written in the paper, before the words fell onto it. That's no consolation. Nothing happens by chance. There is no mistake. When I wanted to send a telegram: 'All is well. I like myself. So you can love me without being afraid,' things turned against me. The post office closed as I arrived, time passed faster than I could; I ran but I had lost too much time, and as soon as I went down a street, it slowed down and finally stopped completely. As if the world wanted to prevent me from getting closer to myself. At the crucial moment. Or wanted to take the blame for me. Spare me. Accuse me. Protect me from myself by splitting me, disarming me. In case there was danger of death. Of silence. Of never arriving. Of arriving at the wrong time. If the post

46

office had been open I could have cabled: 'Can't talk any more. Tongue dead. Once again. Trust.' But I wouldn't have found the words. If God had received the letter, would she have understood any better than I?

When nothing makes sense any more, everything that can feel writhes in pain, everything that supports you collapses, no point in wanting to call out: no one to hear, no one there any more. Paths turn back on themselves. Even if there were someone to receive the letter, with eyes to read it; if you had managed to write what you wanted to write; if there had been paper and he had the strength to bear the pain you are communicating to him: 'Impossible to wait—senseless—no one there,' the suffering would have got worse, paths would have got tangled up, I would have got further away from you, further away from myself, nearer and nearer to no one. But I wanted to assure you 'All is well,' implore you 'I like myself. Please love me without being afraid,' warn you, threaten you with love, with death, so delicately—and the post office was shut.

If I had got there in time, I couldn't have written: 'Beloved, *I* am sure but things are so uncertain,' for words have turned bad, they've turned into bloodhounds. I did so want to warn him: 'Beloved, impossible to move. I won't be able to talk to you any more. Above all don't come here. The pack of words are unleashed.' But I didn't dare to open my mouth. When I wanted to swear, my tongue had an accident, the pack of words escaped on the scent of my blood. And now they are doing their dirty work and making their filthy prophesies, blaspheming and lying right inside my own mouth. And I vomit. They are not ashamed to relieve themselves in front of you—that's why it is just as well the post office is shut. If I were to say everything I've kept back, packs of dogs would hurl themselves after me, biting their tongues in frenzy. Their letters run towards the one I love, they are rushing to pour out their sense. These words aren't words. And *I* would bite him too. Don't say 'I.' Stop your ears. Stuff your mouth with paper. Chew up all the words. Names must be suppressed.

When the fourth day dawned, impossible to remember who to be. Like when you can't come back into your body after a dream: having turned into someone else so that you *are* someone else! And yet life goes on, you pass your shop, you don't have the right to go in any more, because you have the eyes of a woman but the face of a bloodhound. No dogs allowed. You wander round the overcrowded cities with your eyes open, and everyone else has his eyes shut.

Yesterday you were still young, you lived, trusted, were trusted. You didn't see the end of the world. I didn't even know there was an end. Everything was open, hope was allowed. With your eyes shut you desired, you wanted to write, you wrote, you thought your letters went off, arrived. Words were strung together, trees were planted. No doubt. Faith. Things well set up, various, interesting. Sense kept your heart beating. And you so longed to touch his hand that you thought you were already touching it, already caressing it with your eyes, your head already between his breasts—a longing that was a belief. To which everything is to be sacrificed. Especially disbelief.

You can be certain: if you are waiting for him, he is waiting for you too. The same wait. Nothing can separate you. If you feel slightly anxious, it's just a question of visibility. It's a bit misty. But all the signs point to his desire being your desire. The one you love has made exactly the same decision as you: to wipe out the space between us by the fastest possible means, so that we can again be mouth to mouth, word for word. There is the Letter. Certainty. Your whole body tensed to the call. The harp strings are tuned. Same tune. My longing is certainly the same as his. Amen. The car: the one he left for me, is itself pressing you and is worthy of our needs. Such a powerful racing car that it is already making the scenery shudder under its wheels. Nothing is missing. The documents are ready. The keys were put on the table. You only have to get behind the wheel and take off, like the wind. When your

48

goal is adored you don't even see the road, nor the countryside. You feel the lightning speed of horsepower, flesh is drunk, sex seething, teeth sparkle, space is eaten away. Anticipate the smile that will greet you in a moment—you don't even have to anticipate it any more, you can already see it, are there, lost in it.

But this morning you can't see yourself leaving. And yet all the signs point that way. Exactly, it is the signs that are holding up your departue. They are so urgent that they intimidate you. For example: too many keys. Each one prettier and stranger than the next; you can't choose any more and you waste hours examining them. Precisely the best hours. And when you want to slide behind the wheel you notice that the space is too narrow, your woman's hips are too wide, you are disturbed. It's not serious. A slight discrepancy. An illusion of the senses. 'And what if I wasn't a woman?' That is a dangerous idea, it's a Hooker, don't listen to it, it will lead you astray. I followed up the bad idea to avoid the worst. It's a question of trust: if things forsake us, who is at fault? If it isn't your fault, it's his fault. Therefore it's your fault. Two ideas occurred to me. The one with the head of a Hooker at its tail-end said to me: 'It's not the man who is wrong, it's that you aren't a woman any more.' The worst idea said to me: 'Why did he leave you so many keys if not to hold you up? Why did he suggest a booby-trapped car? You were being carried away by your longing, faster than time, and now your heart has broken down, your body is stunned, you don't even dare to say a word in case your tongue explodes; you clench your teeth to stop yourself from spitting out the name you used to call the one-who-is-not-who-he-is.' On the tail-end of that idea was the body of a peacock. It spread its tail in front of your eyes. When I looked down I saw its feet were black and deformed. It collapsed straightaway, its feathers fell. All that was left was a worm slithering away.

I let the Hooker lead me into anguish, for love of him. In order not to lose trust. Rather lose your head. Rather lose

49

sight of it, but still remember you did have it. Rather lose your reason than the truth. Before leaving I sent off two messages in two different directions, on the off chance. 'Distraught. Too many keys. Lost sight. Come and get me.' And 'Beg you to tell me who you are; if possible who I am to you.' I had two voices in my throat, one for cursing, the other for pleading and I tried to get them in tune. Why did you desert me? A woman's blood but the head of a Hooker dancing in front, followed by all your sufferings, all the shapes of lovers surprised in their sleep by your dream of death—who wake up in exile. You are in such pain, it's much greater than you, that it's as if, throughout the ages, there was only one woman to be burnt. And in your flesh all the women in whom you have suffered before, old wound, new pain, the last time wasn't the last, wounded again, only one wicked thought, but it is spread by anguish and all the others are infected. When things aid and abet evil spreads like the wind: your last-born thought is condemned, all these thoughts come by the same route, since the Great Fear; through the bloodstream into the heart, where you are begging, right up to the throat damaged by bitter words, into the eyes where they would like to dart reproachful, remorseful looks at you, if they could catch sight of you. But sight is lost. That Hooker is driving us mad. 'He hasn't changed, it's you who were wrong about him.' Where's the mistake? In your skin. Between us. Among your desires and, like the Hooker, it lives in the streets, in fear, leads us astray, at night it hides in your dreams and is followed by your Longing from the time of the Great Weariness: as if there was only one nest in the whole wide world to return to, to die. The mistake is hiding in your veins, goes right up into the brain to the origin of the Great Fear. Hides in time. Between the 15th and the 25th. He is not wrong, it's time that's changed. One day for another, the wrong day pretends to be the right day, you no longer know which day you are. Where's the 20th? Too late. Not later than Tuesday, probably Thursday. The time has come, the day is breaking, he will go out, the night is in labour, he is keeping you waiting and waiting. The belly of the night is swollen, the head is not engaged, you push and push, the belly is pale, disturbing— when things begin badly they don't ripen, they rot. The birth is a nightmare, they break the water sack with tongs, but there is no water, no child, a monster comes out, it's a Mistake.

Who made it? A bad night. Absence must have come visiting. A germ of Fear, a seed of Hatred, a second of Weariness, a drop of Anguish—when the womb is infected out come Delusions of all kinds.

Ravishers of our souls and our children. Women's legs with sharp-pointed claws. Hookers' heads with a woman's eyes at the tips of their tails. Like Hookers they haunt our ante-rooms with the other monsters in our bellies, with our harpies, in the entrance to our hells; they spread their tails on our beds and we can only see the beloved's body through their crazy eyes. They soil it with their tears and excrement, make us a sheet of shit, and the flesh of the one you adore turns black and falls off his bones. 'The man you love is no longer the same. His Strong Breast is rotten. Why haven't you buried him?' The monstrous delusions all come by the same route since the Great Suffering scene, because of death. They come right up to the bed where you are searching for him; you don't find him; you chase round the whole night looking under the sheets, turning over the blankets, digging around; you plunge in, burrow, worm your way forwards, go through room after room, through generations, as if you never wanted to get up again. You go from bed to bed as if you never wanted to go away—to him, for fear of waking up—in exile. Because you think there is only one bed in the whole wide world where you could lie down to live, get up in your place, and find the man with the smile alive in his place, still safe and sound and kind to you—but this bed has been lost. Because of Guilt. You are banished! And since the accident, all the beds where you go astray go mad while you are asleep, betray you, turn you over

51

to the ants, cut off your eyelids, pierce your throat with needles. You are haunted by delusions, they take away your children and your desires, and those they can't carry off they trample on; they crush your soul, shatter your memories, disfigure their faces; everything is transformed, the Hookers work with the word-hounds with no trouble at all: they beget murders in the bed where you come into being for him; our heads are filled with corpses, you have the body of an old cow and you feed on dead calves, you ruminate and choke down your beloved, like bread, and feed on the children of your womb.

When you sneak out of your mind you breed lion-dragons. When you are chased out dogs, rats and the offspring of mousers emerge.

Where does the delusion come from? From all the sufferings which are roused at night by the birth of a new pang; they are instantly let loose, hang together and they have but one idea: to go back through the bodies they are harming, from bed to bed, back to the first tomb. And they take you along, a prisoner, drag you from body to body, bring you right up to the treacherous bed where love falls upon love as the cat pounces on the mouse, as god herself falls upon her creatures. And wide awake, you are destroyed by dreams, as on the day of the Great Suffering.

Here is the Horriginal scene: You have been careless. Nothing serious. Yet fatal. It happened so fast. I thought I was doing the right thing. Like killing your mother to save her: to stop death approaching her; to stop her seeing death approaching.

This is such a brutal scene that afterwards no one has the strength, nor the heart, nor the tongue, to tell it. And no one knows the truth. Because, during this scene what was true has become false; doubt has made itself at home with certainty as if they were made for each other—you could say night was day and no one would argue. All the species cohabited, bastards came out on all sides, women could give birth through their noses, men through their eyes—no one to rouse the world from such a nightmare. No one could be sure that this horror was just a dream. Who would have the courage to find out?

In the night when I wanted to sleep, slugs invaded my bed; they came in steady waves, in close ranks. The moment I put out the light they climbed up from the depths of the earth. I felt the room swaying, I was convulsed with disgust. I groped for the light switch in the dark—an indescribable experience, for there were regiments of slugs on the wall and I knew they would be even more terrifying in the light, but they would have a different meaning. I put on the light, half dead with the effort, and it was worse: my hand was sticky, they weren't slugs but tongues writhing in pain—god knows whose mouths they had been snatched from. They weren't climbing, pain had driven them mad, they were whimpering and screeching, clashing in blood, falling over each other, biting with their little teeth, rolling into foaming balls, belching and spewing out insults, cries of vengeance, as if I had torn them out and all the resentment in the world was railing against me. I couldn't defend myself, my tongue was stiff as a poker. Anyway, I had nothing to say. Because of my anguish. I myself was bleeding from hatred, blood running out of all my mouths. When truth goes mad, tongues are slaughtered throughout the land, and this goes on until all the tongues wanting to tell the truth are butchered.

I wanted so much to yell, to call on god the mother for help, in the middle of the night I wanted to wake him in broad daylight so that he would come back through the centuries, despite his weariness, despite the distance; for once he wouldn't be stopped by anything, just this one time—but such an important crucial time. I wanted to call god back across the world—I wanted him to do this for me, once, despite his mountains and seas and creation plans;

53

implore him, ask the impossible, just once: I wanted god to come running through his peoples, without being stopped by time-hallowed obstacles, to reverse his history, go over the heads of his people, without hesitating, part the seas with a kick, brush away adorers as if they were flies, not to care about his children and descendants. If his family close in on him I want him to push them away, just this once, break away from their grasp without hesitation—for this is certainly an emergency; if they link arms to encircle him in fleshly bonds to clasp and absorb him, he must force them to let go with a sharp blow to the crook of the elbow. If there is a woman holding him back, serving him, lavishing care on him, he must not let himself be stopped; if the woman bars his way he must not play for time; if the door is shut, get out over the roof; if the woman throws herself in his path, crush her; if she threatens to take her life, he mustn't even let her finish, but set off that very moment. Nothing could put him off, if he heard me howling, no one to argue with him, no obligations to create. If his creature, she for whom he creates, started to yell, to warn him if I shouted: 'This time I really mean it. Please come immediately. Danger of death.' And straightaway, without pausing, because the time had come, that very night, the last time, as if there were no one else in the world, he would set off, any way he could. If there's no earth, invent it, if the earth doesn't go fast enough, leave it behind, take off, if there's no road, make one, invent it with feet, hands, arms, passion, necessity—because it would be impossible for god the mother not to answer, if it were the Promised Time, and if I had shouted out the terrifying truth: 'The tongues have accused me. Impossible to clear myself. Too much blood, no blood left, no sense left. No bed left to die in. Come and take me away.' Nothing could prevent him from rushing headlong. As if he had only given birth to one single Creature in his History. For there is only one real death for us, through scene after scene: the thief who takes advantage of absence to attack, to part us—alive. If I die, god dies. As if he could lose his life

54

once only, if my death robbed him of his life.

I wanted to shout all this and be instantly sure that he heard; not to mind the blood any more, to be able to detach myself, rise above the tongues, ignore what the blood means. Trust. Patience. Steel yourself. You need all your strength. To make your bed in his body tonight.

But when I opened my mouth, no cry came out; while I was taking a breath, anguish rushed into my mouth, disappeared into the vestibule of my ear, my tongue took fright, turned inside out like a glove, rolled over like a snake, bit its own tail, slipped off like a rat through the back of my throat—and I swallowed it live. At the last second—no time even to throw myself to the ground—the terrifying voice of caution shouted: 'Don't call out! What if God herself had gone mad too?'

No cry! My tongue shrivelled up. Don't doubt. Don't check. Don't call out. Be saved. Never know anything. Be sure. Never doubt. Anything. There is some doubt. It's not me. My tongue catted. Because of doubt, with its mad-cat body, its motley coat.

When the world is sick with love, things that held together fall apart, the rot sets in: one hand is afraid of the other, your limbs are frightened of each other, they all have claws. Your desires, which you cherished, turn back into rats and people are afraid to open their mouths because they don't trust their tongues. Who knows what filth might come out? In bedrooms, behind beds, the curtains are big with monsters, animals, strange, disgusting species. Days that liked each other yesterday have seen their end. Horror! Peacocks have ugly, black feet and nights are full of worms at their tail-end. Disgusted at the sight of themselves, the young healthy, fair days have died. Horror! They are tearing their hair. All the vanity and falsehood of this world has hit them in the eye and their eyes roll in terror. Days want to run away from their nights. One hand attacks the other and claws open the palm. How can you help loathing the future when tongues unleash packs of words, with rats at their tail-ends? How can you fail to feel in your gut a longing to tear out the tongue that spits out: 'He will not come. Will never ever be there again to take you in his arms. Will die.' With my fingers? Grasp it in your hand, cut it to the root with an axe.

You will not doubt. If a doubt arises, give it the fate it deserves. No doubt. I lay awake in anguish. Hunger stopped me sleeping. The Hunger of Hungers. Fruitless waiting. The flesh fell off my bones. You eat yourself up with worry, do all you can to stop up the holes; during the fast, Lent, you eat everything that's good, bad or indifferent, animals slaughtered by the hands of Moors, Jews, humans, the sick, bread made by the insane, all fats and tender, untamed flesh. Nothing stays the hunger. The earth can't make ends meet any longer. Food turns traitor. And what tortures you most is not hunger, not the impossibility of knowing whether there will be an end to all this, but the fact that you suspect that by eating, you are not feeding yourself but your Hunger.

To your great shame, right in the middle of one of these senseless meals, the memory of a painful scene often recurs, from the time of the Great Famine: it was not a dream. A rat emerges so fast, as if shot from a canon. It hadn't had time to go a yard before I was upon it. And I soon slit it open to get straight to the flesh. So what . . .

What's wrong with that? Others would have done what I did. I didn't go rat catching. I am not wholly responsible, the rat appeared in a moment of crisis and anyone else would have done the same. Would have pounced on it. More brutally than a tiger. More unerringly than a woman at bay. More inexorably than doubt on love. And without waiting a second, it begins to . . .

Here the memory fades, it's not clear.

I had been through all that before. Experienced it before. Related it before. Doubted before. Destroyed before. Puked up before.

As soon as I had opened up its breast I tore out its heart and threw it into the street. The world had shrunk: it was contained in that flesh, the black blood; reduced to the meat which was life itself. Why shouldn't I eat a rat, taste it without hesitating, when all the cats do.

It would be better if this were a fiction. At that time there was no difference. No wall, no skin, visions hurled themselves at your eyes in broad daylight, and bit at them. All cats were rats in the dark and the rats could be anyone. If you mistake your craving, who's at fault? Who will pay for it? Who will play the rat in love's place?

But as for the horriginal scene, firstly, no hunger. There is bread, milk and light. Doors. Ways in. Ways out. You can move. Tracks lead somewhere. To the end of the line and back, how simple everything was. And hands. Real hands. Touching hands. *Hands*. Cryptic. Inside: your life lines, your paths of action; within: the little bed for your desires. The best part of the body for knowing everything. Your 'I' is in your hand. The universe in the palm of your hand. The hand doesn't forget that it is the most amorous part of the body and the body is in the hollow of the hand. Caressed. Hand-picked. The earth too, then, gathered together inside your skin, not a crumb left out, hand-sewn edge to edge, no abyss, mouths full of tongues. In the palm. And all the caresses meant for you, coming towards your body from the beginning of time, come through the hands of the Same Man. You had that body. You remember. You have lost it.

It happened in a flash: you are walking in a garden with the man who is your mother. Suddenly the earth quakes. A split. He holds his hand out to you and says: 'Take my hand. It's not serious. Jump.' You would like to jump. You would like to take his hand. Obey him. Cross over. Be with him forever. You don't want to be parted by a hair's breadth from the one who nourishes you. But the moment your muscles tighten, the instant you are about to hold out your hand, at that infinitesimal moment which hasn't yet split you, the voice of caution speaks: 'Stop! Be careful! Have you taken all the necessary precautions? Are you capable of taking the leap? That wound doesn't look too good. Can't you see it's getting bigger? What is it about that split really?' And the voice also says: 'You should think of his well-being. What if the earth split as you were going over? Supposing it gaped open and swallowed us up? Who says it's not serious? You should know when to pause. This caution is not a bad thing. You are hesitating because of love.' All this in a split second. You look up, hold out your hand. But he has withdrawn his. He isn't looking at me, he is not smiling at me. His face is strange, as if the light had gone out of it. His skin pale, cheeks, forehead motionless, craggy, the blood drained from his face. He hasn't opened his mouth. The silence in the world around was terrifying: as if I had struck at its voice and the world had died of the blow. And yet I wasn't armed. No iron instrument, no stone, no fatal blow. Without hostility. Without thinking. Accidentally. Unintentionally. And inspired by love. But what if love listens to fear? As a precaution? His face in profile. His eyes turned away from me. As if she-whom-he-is-waiting for, for whom he stays alive, was not in your place but out of sight, over there where you are not, on the other side of the frontier. And the one who is here, where my body is drained of sense, arms cut off, the whole person cut off from space where things are bright and changing, *is not looked at*. Not seen. Invisible. If he looked you in the face now, you would read love's decree on his brow; you would burn with shame; you would be consumed with horror. But he doesn't look at you, you don't die. But you don't exist. Driven away into the infinite where you cannot even die.

What happened? A trifle. A split. A miscalculation. The earth had a tear in it. I was afraid the tear would stretch and turn into an abyss, but I'd got the wrong body: while I was examining the earth it was my flesh that split open. In a flash, belly opened up, a huge wound. As soon as I looked at the lips of the wound which were black and ugly, my strength left me, I was overcome with disgust, I had to step back so I wouldn't throw myself in. Black blood ran out. All my courage seeped away. It was very cold in the garden. Your tongue was already hurting. Your throat almost frozen. Eyes hard as stone. Belly festering.

Not a delusion. A rift. Things that have begun terribly badly end in bad blood. When a woman feels doubt, she should go and live apart. She shouldn't walk on the earth, touching the man who is her mother. She shouldn't soil the universe because she is unclean. I was pure. I had never felt doubt. The earth quaked. Blood ran out of the body. I didn't even know doubt existed in life. Suddenly, at my feet, a flow of blood. I shuddered. The milky Voice of Innocence was silent. Who killed it? Not me. The earth. I looked down: a split! Blood on the edges of the wound. Nothing serious. A ditch. If the world is bleeding anything can happen! Just a ditch. Not even a chasm. Because of a crack. For love. But love was wrecked. Because of death. There was doubt in the flesh, under the skin, between the breasts, but you didn't suspect it. This love was too human. You had no suspicion.

When does doubt arise? The moment you take the plunge. A blunder, you have no experience. Innocence is guilty. You hold out your hand. Doubt takes it.

He was talking to you face to face, he called you, smiling, took your tongue in his mouth and you answered it with yours—and his life-giving tongue in your mouth: 'Come, take my hand.' But you withdrew your tongue, you didn't give your hand, anguish came back into your head through your ears, you swallowed its words like whey, crap, tasting of tenderness.

He said to you: get up! I leapt up. No need to be careful where I put my feet. If he said: jump, that meant life is on the other side; just one step and you are across. That's what you are made for. I came to life instantly! In response to his voice: go forward, turn left, lean down, turn the page, up, to the right, I took him at his word. Lived 'to the letter': mine: my body which he is reading. Everything had been written by his hand, according to my need. To my amazement, when I wanted to jump my body did not obey. The word held it back: the letter arrived, the symbols were strange, the ink seemed paler. Instead of jumping I thought twice. Because the body is weak.

Where does doubt come from? It doesn't come. It is not something that arrives. The word arrives without a sound. Your glance hovers round objects without getting through. Sight is off-target. Vision fails. Conflict of views. Things near you are too restless, you see them tossing about. You are not blind enough. Everything that should have remained hidden is revealed, the world's private parts, its strange organs, shameful beasts, suddenly looked at, memory's gone wrong: what should have been left out takes its revenge; you commit the crime of remembering what should be forgotten. You remember all the victims that had to be sacrificed throughout the centuries for the earth to stay firm under your feet. You see them naked, the brood of fears, your mother's daughters, love's excrement, its abominable offspring, your own vermin, the litter of disturbing thoughts that you had driven from your flesh, the fruits of your coupling with the dead, your brood of rats—they were not far away—all it needs is the earth to quake, the sheet slides off, uncovers them, and you see them swarming around, not dead but very much alive—your eyes opposite the gaping holes you would rather not see. But everything happens as if, instead of looking straight ahead, instead of caressing things, contemplating the duration of love, you made the holes yourself, you tore things apart, forced your way in, destroyed. With the eyes of a lion-dragon.

*

60

It was the first day of August. A terrifyingly brutal incident occurred. I was walking in a city in a foreign land. The man who is my mother was walking beside me. My hand in his hand. His hand was trembling. I didn't know why. And if I had known? I certainly wouldn't have understood, because his reasons were not human. The man in whose breast I was living was God herself, and God's language was beyond me. My hand was trembling too; I adored him, even the earth was quaking under our feet; roads turned aside. 'This sickness is not fatal. Two or three days without news. I'll go to bed, get up. That's certain.' I was certain. Two people came running up and hurled themselves in front of us. I had seen them another time, in another life. The man with the Breast was smiling, his hand vibrating in mine, I was terrified. When you see them it's a sign. They spoke to me in the language of adultery. Neither male nor female, stinking, full of mischief. Eagles' talons on the tips of their tongues. They flung out biting words passing on madness and doubt and the diseases of love. Why I understood this language was only too clear to me: I too must have spoken it, when I was dirty. I must have been dirty enough, long enough for it to come back so easily. But I didn't remember. It must have been 'in another country.' I must have talked this crap in another body. I was sad as in a dream. Who knows what lives I had led, before I was born, what corpses I had dragged round in, what memories soiled me, what vices? Who knows in what bestial ways I had lived when I was still rotten, on what stakes my flesh roasted on the spit? If I were guilty, it wasn't my fault any more. Huge cars surrounded us, we couldn't go on. These people burst out: 'Can't you see he is dead.' The monsters were obese, they didn't have bodies but skins crammed with rubbish. 'Why do you think we are here? He doesn't even notice.' Take me, eat me up, but don't look at him! Pus ran out of all their seams. 'Did you think you'd forgotten us? We'll never forget you!' They were laughing, they had mouths all over their bodies, abcesses bursting on their breasts and

61

emptying under my eyes. Their sacks of skin swollen with rotting desires. I saw their tongues shitting. Shitting out their hatred all over them. Their jealousy filling their pants.

They dirtied themselves in the language of death. 'We have come back to fuck you.' They slung at me all the words that paint the world in muck. I had never heard them before and now here they were coming back into my ears; they perforated my eardrums, pierced my brain reaching love's bed—and my soul understood them. As if I had been one of them before I loved. Their pus-filled language must have been my first language of death. 'The one you love is rotten. He is already decomposed. His Strong Breast has caved in. She can't even see! We had met before on a more familiar ground where they were squatting on another bed, shitting. 'He is sick. He is going to die.' He went on smiling. I didn't believe them. I swear. I resisted. But I wanted to protect him. I didn't want him to hear: 'Go away! Go away!' But I didn't dare speak. I didn't know what tongue was in my mouth. They communicated the Worst to me in this language and I took it. I ought to have run away, put land and seas between them and us; I didn't dare move for fear of worrying the man with the smile. I wanted to stab them, cut their throats, stick knives into them, give their tongues to the vultures. Instead, I watched them humbly. I bargained with lion-dragons! 'You can eat up my right hand, my right arm if you like, but don't touch my left hand because it is in the hand of the loved one.'

I didn't want them to touch him. Sweat was oozing from every pore. When you are frightened to death you regret everything. You don't know where to take cover any more, you don't know what death to trust. 'Kill me! Tear me to pieces. Take my body between your teeth. Crush me. But not in front of him. Not now.' As if I were selling myself to the harpies. The monsters made me stagger My left hand paralysed in the hand of the loved one. The obese monsters were blackmailing me: 'An arse for an arse.' I would have given my tongue and heart too.

I began to beg them: 'Be quiet! Leave him alone! Leave us alone! One last time.' Such an effort to make myself heard! My throat resisted. Tear out the sounds one by one, my tongue bleeding, mouth full of galling words, as if I were drinking my mother's blood and spitting it out again. Blood rushed to my head. I didn't know what I was saying any more. I was drunk with terror. I was so afraid that they would remind me what I might have done when I spoke the same crap as them. Afraid they would bring me back to death. Say in their piercing voices, with tongues like sharp claws: 'The devil's got your tongue. He fucked you. We are here to bear witness.' I had to stop them telling me: 'You licked his arse. You ate bucketsful of shit. Riding his vain cock there was no stopping you, you plunged into body after body till you dropped into the body of a bitch-hyena, full of shit.' I would have agreed to everything they wanted. I would have admitted the excrement; made obscene movements; confessed to all the stinking memories torn from their bowels; I would have made all the gestures necessary to stop myself from being taken away from the man with the smile. I would have licked the devil's arse. Caressed his cock from tip to tail; sucked his terrifying tool. I would have gone back through the species, right down to the dregs. To keep the monsters quiet. I would have made hate with a lion-dragon.

The harpies came closer, I was lying on a tomb, they forced their tongues between my lips, right down to the heart and I puked up: everything they wanted. 'He is sick. He is dead. He is rotten.' Yes. Yes. 'You have come to bury him.' '—Do as you like.' 'You can sleep. No need to wake up. All beds lead to the man and the man leads to death.' Yes, yes. Repeat everything death says. To satisfy it, so that death spares the loved one —dead or alive. My love, don't listen, it is for you that I doubt. If I give my tongue to be cut out, it's for love. The harpies are tearing it to shreds, it's no longer an organ, it's a wound. I am bleeding for you, death got my tongue, I sucked up to death, promised to sleep with death in our bed. 'But not today, tomorrow, afterwards, another day, I promise.' If he were dead, dying, when he wouldn't know; so that he doesn't know what's going on. He had said to me: 'Nothing can happen to me.' I believed him. It's death that terrified me. It was my first day of doubt. Crafty old anguish: you don't even realize you are doubting; you think you are trusting; and trust is already put out. Unhappiness has come from within to examine love with the crazy eyes of a lion-dragon. To see if love is stronger than the beasts who envy us, fascinate us and force us to live with the dangerous longing to step on death's tail—just to see.

Jump! How you want to receive that command, not to receive it, to forestall it, to leap in the garden, almost before it was flung out, and pass in one bound into immortality. You would like not to obey, not to doubt, but to have carried out the order in advance! For love.

But the body has changed. This one doesn't know how to leap forward. And when it changes it is weak and hopeless.

Outwardly I look like a woman. But instead of looking him in the face I looked askance at him. I got love wrong. I was afraid to look at him through the eyes of death. Afraid of being seen as I feared I looked, and yet I didn't know what kind of being I could possibly look like—with the animals frightening me, tormenting me, going through me and disfiguring me; I didn't know what other being had taken my place, with or without my consent. If I was looking askance at him, wasn't it so that he could put me straight?

His eyes did not save me. Everyone was looked at but me. So it's not me any more who is in front of him? There was a woman beside him, he didn't take her for me, but she had my heart inside her. *She* was the other, but *I* was the one in pain. You never know who the other is. She seemed dead-looking to me. And I was—nailed by the heart. It seemed to me I had suffered this way before: being in death's place; seeing death in the place of the man with the smile.

I had succeeded before in smashing life's face in. I had

achieved what is impossible for a human being: playing in the garden with a knife for so long, with such passion, that you are won over by the knife, seduced by the sense of the knife, until you let yourself be captured by it. And suddenly you turn into the knife, you get up and with a mad thrill plunge yourself ten times into your mother's body, drunk with daring, and masturbate to death.

Break out of yourself by force, or by sins of omission. As in this mysterious incident, for example:

When you come to think of it, nothing can explain my gesture, no reason, no excuse—an unjustifiable caprice. Not pleasure, not necessity, not professional duty. I didn't think. The Saintly Breast who was nourishing me had said: 'Wait for me here. I won't be long. Death doesn't take long. I'll be back.' I went out. Was I alarmed, carried away by hunger? No. I didn't need anything. And yet I took a few steps down the street. It was a foreign land. I went forward. As if nothing had happened. What does 'as if' mean, in this case? But there was no one to think about it. 'Stay where you are. Sleep and create us in your dreams. It's such a small world.' I go out, take a few steps down a street and it's over. It was the first morning in August. The city was not attractive. It was so insignificant, it was hardly there. I was disappointed. The world was so cramped. I didn't go far. Three steps and it's already evening; such pale people around me that they merge into one another. Already night-time. That is when—was it because of the wall close by, or the night coming on?—I see myself, I see the frontier, I see the end, I see I am outside. And straight ahead of me, two steps away, I see the Saintly Breast in person. He stares at me, motionless, as if he couldn't see me—as if he were dead, or I had no face. And death flew at my throat. 'It's a mistake!' 'It's an illusion!' 'It's a dream!' It was a betrayal.

I didn't know why the Saintly Breast had decided to bring death into the world—like an eclipse. Everything was up to

65

me. When such a Great Saint withdraws, she who cares about his departure goes through hours of absolutely unique suffering. The cruellest things are asked of her: to go with him to the end of the road which is taking him away from us forever; to believe he will come back alive; to carry out his wishes in a world that's out of joint; to point out his greatness, his gentle, boundless presence, because, while you are making preparations, normal life carries on, but the Saintly Breast has halted between the life which is no longer his and the one he has ordered. To the world he is no longer there, to me he had never been so intensely present, everywhere: his splendour envelopping me, clothing me, his purity spreading through my veins, my thoughts, he is inside me, like love. Only his body is missing. I made the necessary gestures, there were endless formalities, I went from office to office, I was suffering; I thought of him as he still was, stretched out in his room, having already left behind all ties with everyday life—in transition. He wasn't ill, he was leaving. Prepare for the break. Have the poster printed for his last message. If I dared I would have begged him to take me into his bed. I was weak. I was afraid he was mortal. That was unthinkable. I would have begged him to take me with him, even to his death, even if it wasn't death. But I would have offended him. It wasn't just a selfish desire: I was haunted by fear of his loneliness. It was a selfish desire: I was haunted by fear of such great loneliness. But I was even more afraid of fear.

Is that an explanation? Not at all. Once outside I didn't feel any of these torments. I would not have gone out if there had been a reason to. I would have destroyed it, for love.

It has always been like this: betrayal without a motive. How do you betray unawares? Finding it out too late? How do you kill from afar without touching anyone. You don't know. You are condemned to commit the crime that you cannot commit —you would rather die than carry it through. Everything is arranged so that it is impossible *not* to commit it, as if it had been committed in advance, for you, against you, instead of you, by someone else, in your absence. Guilt needs you. But you won't give yourself up alive. Might as well give in to death. Who would do that? You only give in to your longing for death when you are already dead. Already lost. Perhaps by mistake, because you have trouble seeing, you take the man with the smile for death, because they look vaguely alike, but not enough, not enough. Or, by accident, you read the last page of the Book of the Dead and find your own name in it! And you suddenly learn that you are marked out. It is written: you are dead—what are you waiting for to die, to join flesh and name? And despite yourself, you feel guilty as usual because you always feel ashamed when your name has been called and you have been late in answering the summons. Is it your name? It is. A bit pale, a bit aggrieved, but you recognize your beloved's hand—writing. It's your fault if the letters are a little jumbled, the beloved must have got impatient. Hurry up and kill yourself.

You go out in your sleep. A dream convinces you that you are not outside but asleep in bed. There's a shadow shadow-playing you in the street; it hops along, half rat, half me, darker than you; and the streets, turning back on themselves, mislead it. How small the womb is, you think you are going on for an eternity, you run, eyes shining in the dark, you smell blood, suddenly the end, you smell cat, the jaws open. Already! What an awakening: wrenched with the utmost violence out of non-being, unconsciousness, re-called to Yourself by the Worst happening. And what a worst! An apparently harmless hour with its fangs bared: you have run so fast, so unerringly towards death. What hour? The hour when walls desert us. The irony of a light in the middle of the night, and you have no choice but to see your body in that light; you can't prevent yourself from answering the summons, going to the window so that it gapes open; you see yourself flinging yourself out, half dead with fright, just as you are, wet feet, hair tangled, not dressed, covered in dreams—dreams everywhere, at your throat. You can't stop yourself condemning, executing; you know where you've got to; you are half mad with a strange longing to be consumed at last. As if you had only gone through life innocently so you could be more easily sacrificed in the end. You have delayed as long as possible on the way, exasperating he who has been waiting for you forever. So that there is no answer to the accusation. So that everything is carried out according to your most ambiguous plans: you could only die condemned. It's as if you were afraid of bungling your death; of dying on the sly one day or another, never mind where, without pleasing the man to whom every drop of your blood is dedicated. As if you were afraid of dying without giving your consent, without wishing to beforehand; in order to anticipate the decision of the man with the breast. So that all the ways of the one you love, even the dead-ends, are vindicated. If I were you I would be merciless, I'd make short work of it. I wouldn't play around. I wouldn't play cat and mouse. No shamming. Do it for real. No use lying: everything is true. The truth is that the rat only draws back to entice the cat to pounce. Your mother only let you run free so she could pounce on you later. Sometimes you go out to get out, sometimes to lose yourself so you can be found, at times you want to be lost, depending on the time and how you feel—the truth is, you never can get out. And another truth is that you suspect you want to be condemned so that you can sin more freely. As long as it is only a suspicion you are probably right, but as soon as you accuse yourself directly, it is false. Because the truth is that you can only ever commit the crimes you feel you are the author of by default. The only possible victim of all the murders we are made to commit in order to live is the woman you become when the man with the Smile says to you: 'Wait for me. I'll be back in an hour. Three or four lifetimes at the latest.'

You go out for an hour. Three lifetimes pass. You are still running. The city is endless. What a distance! And you leave

68

everything behind. You forget. One more leap. And the time is up!

Oh! How everything comes back then! Mother! The Saintly Breast! I was to see him this morning. The Smile. At ten o'clock. But he wasn't there at ten. That's why I went out. For a minute. Did you think of him at ten? I went out without thinking. Without anguish. Actually, without dressing. My legs carried me away. I intended to get some air, to clear out. Given that I had a body, all muscles and no anguish. 'Doubtless he didn't come.' You say that, doubting. Certainly he came. Doesn't he always do what he says? You went out, rashly, like a mouse, without a thought in your head—and came back to yourself guilty—it's unbearable. You don't go out on purpose, but you wake up far from Yourself at the time he might have come—do you do it on purpose? The truth is you had forgotten. Who can really say that's true? Not me. I was a mouse at that moment, at the worst a rat. He who knows everything will certainly think so. If he did come. You see how you are? No. The Great Saint would have seen for me. No one forgets. That's the tragedy. No one is guilty. Everyone forgets. We are not forewarned, we forget we can forget. To be robbed in mid-life: taking advantage of a second of absence, in comes 'forgetting'. There's no one there. Because of the separation. Amnesia lies down in the bed unnoticed, in the place of I don't know who any more.

This is how you feel as you come running back. Your whole being is distorted, it isn't love that makes you run and groan, it is fear. Run to your judge, faint with anguish, He won't be there any longer.

It's the same old story: the right hand doesn't know what the left hand is doing. But it is more complicated than that: You aren't just one other self, but you have as many selves as fingers on your two hands. Plus the thumb. All different, no leader. No self is cleaner than the others. You hurl yourself into hell ten ways at once. But it's not me who's burning—it's my other self. And among my others there are some I am closer to intellectually, others through passion, others through sexual confusion. When one goes out all the others follow; when one weeps, she weeps for all of us; when one hits out, all are guilty; if one feels guilty, the others make mistakes for her. That is why, when the court meets, there is always one of us to answer the accusation. And because of one only, all those who represent me—including the youngest, the girls of five years old and under—are in danger of being put to death. In these conditions it is virtually impossible ever to know more than a moment's peace. Too many frontiers. Too many wars. Too many opportunities. And life, from threat to threat, is never certain, is merely 'saved': a close shave, a series of chances and miracles, not a history—mere chance. The tension is so exhausting that one of us always cracks up, loses heart, lets herself be tempted by the easy way out: enters into negotiations with death, makes concessions to death with one hand and takes them back with the other; equivocates, and so is granted a brief, immoral respite, a little indulgence, a pass, 'leave of shame.' Because, actually, the others are there and they will have to pick up the pieces, pull her up, give her a boost—if you want life to go on. And you say 'I', 'I' want, day after night, accused, condemned, put to death, reprieved, pardoned, never acquitted. Living such a brutal life, unwillingly pitted against death, always with someone inside weakening, betraying, selling herself to death, and, if the truth be known, always with a touch of death in your blood, a taste of death on the tip of your tongue and under your nails—you would have given up the fight long ago, stopped trying to begin all over again, if I didn't love you.

I've been through this before. I went out as if nothing were happening. Never had. Never did happen. There are strange moments in the stories of my lives: whole days lived by

70

someone else. In the dark, you take the wrong turning in time: you get up, unawares, slap in the middle of another story, which drags you far away from yourself, while our connections, relationships, memories, all our possessions, have stayed in the usual story from which we are now infinitely separate. You don't realize it because you have the same body and you have been transplanted in your sleep. That's what you think, after the event, to try to justify yourself; but that doesn't alter the intensity of the shame that creeps into your tiniest thought when you wake up—lost. When what gets up at the sun's inexorable insistence is Guilt. No need to look at your watch, you know the time: 'What were you doing?'—'I was forgetting you'—But that's not true.

You sleep. You serve. You do everything you thought you were incapable of doing. Fly. Jump. Speak a foreign language. Teach English in German. Teach pupils of both sexes skills you don't even possess. You go from the impossible to the impossible through all the possibilities of fraud: you fill all the places you have no right to. Whether you like it or not, no one knows, and you don't forget you know nothing either. You are uneasy, at ease, sorry, angry, negative. You owe the right to fill these places to someone else—it's the dark night of your soul—anguish is compelling you to do what fear wants to prevent you doing. You plunge into the mountains as if they were paper curtains, at the helm of escaped monsters. You discover you have a talent for all kinds of delusions, falsehood, crimes. Everything you touch is tinged with remorse. That is not what you wanted: to do everything you didn't want to do, because you dare not disappoint someone you hardly know, whose name you can't even remember. You taste murder like a gourmet, almost faint with disgust. You drink blood and try to upset the glass under the table without being seen. Things gradually get harder and harder. You sink lower and lower. And you don't wake up. What suffering! If it goes on, you won't have the strength to come back—how you'd like to run away! Wake up. But there's still a job to be done. You have promised, you don't know where or when, or to whom, it doesn't matter; what has been said cannot not be done; and you drag to the rendez-vous like a corpse. Another child to butcher, a Great Saint to bury with your own hands while he watches you in sorrow. And you don't overstep the mark: there is no mark. No visible frontier, if only there were. But the more you try and find one the further away it gets, because you want it. You want to shout to the man with the Breast: 'Mother, can't you see I am losing myself? Why don't you wake me up?' They will. One last time. An adultery. This farce can't go on! Who could possibly have made so many commitments? Right and left, with both hands at once. To what judge could you have dedicated so many evil deeds? It's too much! What do you get from all this? All the unhappiness. No one to benefit from it. Who is letting you dream beyond the bounds of self-preservation? Letting you make unforgivable pacts with death? Exchange your right to mother's milk for a dish of grubs and excrement? Who is taking the words out of your mouth when you want to call your mother for help? Who is writing this farce? If the loved one is letting you suffer, who is getting a thrill out of it? Who enjoys being deserted? Forgotten? Lost, as far away as possible from the entrance? Punished over and over again with anguish and insecurity? Who is giving me the dreams that I dare not wake up from? Who is dragging me from fault to fault to the end? They want me to die. I too want to die for someone: a being for whom you are split apart. I would so like to tell him: 'My love, look at all the lives I have lost for you, and now I don't have any left, make me dream of return.' But as soon as I open my mouth, his name escapes me, Amnesia grabs hold of it, swallows it up. All the names that could love me are snatched away, including my own.

Go and search for them, go running from city to city, in anguish—the anguish that turns cities into forests—with the painful feeling that you have been that way before, without

72

being sure; plunge in, don't be checked by any warning, though you are less and less sure. If you really do recognize where you are, it doesn't matter, if you have gone astray here before, you don't remember it. And if, instead of arriving somewhere that you remember, you feel the world closing in, you wonder terrified whether everything has been decreed from the start so that all your attempts to escape bring you back to the foot of the big bed, the place where, while you run as fast as you can along an unpaved path, you begin to think all over again you will end up standing yet again, trembling with weariness—and the bed will be empty. You probably want to forget that you are so desperate now that you haven't the strength to go through such loneliness, to go on searching, or to believe that there will come a day, a way, an hour when you won't be let loose in the void. You want to forget that you long so passionately to stop suffering that all other desires have vanished. You would like to hold on to them, as love wants to cling to the phantom of love, but as soon as it holds out its arms the phantom vanishes. That is why you hold out your arms, it's not really you, just your arms held out—and the shadow flees.

Like the Letter chasing across the page, pursuing the thought that it has never seen full face, not even its backview, but the Letter thinks, is almost sure, that if it caught up with this thought, it would indeed be the one it was expecting: the true one for which it has worn itself out fighting in a frenzy from line to line against the giddiness which is threatening the Letter who is putting death off from word to word, in order to give life, if it exists, the chance, the time, to take its place at last, and who can never be sure, when the suspense is over, when there's not a scrap of paper left and it has reached the end of the world where it was decreed from the start it would end up, whether it has managed to pass on a little sense, not even a wish, a slight tremor; possibly the Letter succeeds, it may send to the unknown thought the symbol that will stop it, hold it without imprisoning it so that it is identified with its fate, as a mother identifies with the fate of her daughter. Because the Letter only wanted to be written down to enjoy its own embodiment. But when the Letter takes hold of the thought tenderly, it is impossible to be sure that it is indeed The Thought, the true one, because after such a long odyssey everything has changed: it is not the same letter and besides, it doesn't know what to make of itself any more; it's forgetting itself. It has never been anything but a passion, the trembling of the paper strained by the thought's efforts to be newly embodied, to put a new face on things. The Letter has never really been anything but the tomb of these thoughts that have failed to be embodied, a confession of anguish, a way of revealing that, in the end, there is only one desire left: to stop suffering.

You seem to have thought all this before, during another search, and as the path moves under your weight, you have the feeling it is going off in the wrong direction. Time must have gone backwards: the further forward you go the further away you get. You remember going astray before, but you can't remember where this aberration leads you. And as you go on you become so exhausted that all you ask for is a breathing space! Any respite—from anyone. But you don't even have the strength left to tell yourself that. So it's easier to forget that instead of managing to remember the name of the man who is the cause of such an accumulation of fears and pain, you have managed—god will know how, even if you don't want to know—to let yourself Forget.

What's wrong with that? Isn't Amnesia extremely courteous? It hands me over to the wolf-dragon, a person half-female, half-bird. But plucked. A bit like a frog, but her back legs are shaped like a man's. She doesn't know anything about my life. The Monster Amnesia invites me to spend a night in her spacious rooms. She's so kind. She came to me in bird's clothing, but plucked. I forgot to protect myself. 'Will you

74

stay the night here?' 'Why not? No harm in that?' No one said to me: 'Be careful of treacherous Lapses who come to you in sirens' clothes and are little whorish frogs inside.' Everything happened in the back. Naturally there was only one double bed. One but not two. That's the trouble with Forgetting. I longed to call out but I didn't know who to call for any more. In case of absence who do you inform? Everything took place as if it had happened before. The scenario had already been written. Someone had read it before. Page by page. But not me. 'You've heard this story before.' Someone else remembered it. I didn't. I said to myself: 'Beware.' Suspicion arose; I didn't know who to suspect any more. I was hesitating in the dark. You could get the wrong past, wrong clothes, wrong style. I was impatient but I couldn't make out what I wanted. My sheep came to me in wolves' clothing. But they were false sheep. Other beasts came in unannounced. Moments overlapped: carts before horses, horses in cat's clothing. Cat-astrophe. Naturally there was only one bed. 'I must speak to the children.' If I had any children I'd know myself by them. Phone. Don't go home. Inform someone in case of Amnesia: 'Don't forget me.' My call came through. What number had I dialled? As if I had called myself I was convinced someone would call back. 'Help me, get me out of here!' I was five years old then, I had a direct line to fear. I wanted to shout out, but I didn't dare in case I offended the wolf-dragon. 'Hallo? Who's speaking?' How I wanted someone to say my name! 'I won't be back this evening,' I murmured. And I am lead to death like a substitute lamb. 'You are going too far.' That was my mother's voice. I was certain. She had recognized me. Who else would have heard me? How I wanted to recognize her, but I didn't know her voice. 'Whom do I have the pleasure of speaking to?' I stammered. Monster, don't hide my names! Words came out of my mouth, I didn't know what they said. Which saint shall I phone? Which mother will answer me? Hallo? My mother's voice in the distance. 'Amnesia's going to put me to bed!' I said. My mother hangs up. Silence. Cut off. I seem to have heard that silence before. Someone I adore is no longer talking to me. I'm very afraid it's my mother. If it isn't her it is her silence, how could I fail to recognize it? As if she had answered me: 'Your name is Shame and your second name is Horror.' I was with the wolf-dragon. Someone phones. I lift the receiver. 'Whom do I have the pleasure of speaking to?' It was the voice of the man with the Breast. A knife cuts my throat. It didn't hurt at all but I felt a great pain—in my heart. Impossible to say a word. 'How long is this farce going on for?' His voice stops me from speaking. 'Help!' my throat wasn't hurt, I could have yelled, but mother had hung up. Silence. Don't let the wolf-dragon see anything. Go on listening to a long silence on the phone that is only deafening me. Evening comes, there is only one bed. No one had told me. What's wrong? It's a big bed. We can both rest on it. The wolf-dragon puts on her lamb's gown. She is very polite. She doesn't ask for much: touch, a little tenderness, complicity without violence. Her little frog-body, her mens' legs, her big sheep's breasts. And I am tall and sad in my stranger's gown. And I am lead to the bed as if to my death. I have been through all this before, hundreds of years ago. You have to go through with it—death and the jackal! She is full of solicitude. I could feel her dugs—what anguish—time to scream, but the phone is cut off. If I could have called you! 'Help, she's going to give me her milk.' Don't do it. Don't soil your name with my shameful tongue. Anyway, your name's escaped me; my thoughts pursued it, croaking like frogs and I prayed they wouldn't catch up with it. My bones turned to jelly, my eyes saw thousands of tiny breasts climbing all over the sheets. It was an illusion. I didn't dare say anything to the wolf-dragon. I collapsed, unable to move, the sheets were moving. I was sure I was wrong: they weren't breasts climbing up the big bed but a kind of bug—the vermin of sin. Madness! Madness! What have I done? Nothing really bad. Thoughts are dangerous. It tears me apart to see the body created for you, up to its neck in the jaws of the Monster Amnesia. What do they want? What do I want? What do the jaws want? I turn over in bed wallowing in Loss. Back turned, curled up, vermin for my shawl. The bed sags. What shouldn't have happened happens: its body rolls against mine because I should have avoided it. I am going to scream. Phone the Saint. I am going to ask him if he is letting me sink on purpose into the Big Bad Bed. 'What Saint?' I am going to say to him: 'Why did you force me to do the worst? And now that I am buried in the wrong Bed who is enjoying my shame?' Someone wants my downfall. If it isn't me it's he who is flinging me onto a dungheap where the dung comes out of his own body—as if I were his excrement. A flood of terror. Who is wallowing in this bed? How have I sunk so low? The whore at my back with her friendly dugs, making me loathe my life. She doesn't know me. I want to tell her about the man who is my mother. Not on this bed, in this pain. I could never tell her. Truthful words wouldn't come out of my mouth alive. The wolf-dragon's innocence, my madness, his treachery. She isn't asking much of me: a bit of flesh, a little blood, a little lying about my fantasy-lover. A little bit of ambiguity. If only I could take off my Amnesia robe just once. Oh God! What have I done to you that you want me to soil myself? Someone wants me to betray. Is God there? I want to speak to him! I am prostrate, my sheep's gown tucked up. Help, my life is slipping away? As it runs off it cries: 'Forgive me, forgive me!' The wolf-dragon smacks my bottom. Who will wipe out my sin? 'Lama Lama Sabactami! I will never forgive you.' Someone wants me to be a monster. I am forced to sin, found guilty—before whom? Who wants to drive me to despair? If it's not you, it's god. So it's me too. I've done all you asked. No one can want that. For love. My sheep's gown tucked up, I am lead to Guilt like a girl to the altar, to the jaws of Amnesia—and my life gown's torn. Gradually, I have become more and more deeply, more and more carnally, tangled up in sheets full of vermin—and under my

77

life gown my vile flesh. Her greedy dugs in my back. And death was gaining ground. I was gradually sucked in by the wolf-dragon's warmth, her greedy little body, her persuasive legs and I backed into the treacherous trap of her polite violence, her breasts sucking me in—I wanted to shriek, what body could I take refuge in? The treacherous sheep's dugs, and underneath: whore's mouths like leeches. I was clasped in her claws with their winged-jackal tips, absorbed little by little. I am promised to death like a child promised to the Monster's devouring sex, part-male, part-female and her incestuous breasts don't bite but have bloodsucker slits. My body passed into her belly. Cleaned out, my thoughts collapsed; my skin tattoed with filth. I surrendered—a succubus. Relieve yourself in the arms of the wolf-dragon. You will be known by your faeces and your fruits.

How could I not be tempted to phone the Strong Breast? Precisely because I had come to a point when I longed for his help; his ear; his life. My craving to complain in the bitterness of my blood and the shit of my body. To describe my scarred skin to God, so he would know me by my vermin. Make a statement of my wounds, so that he could check my accounts.

My craving for forgiveness, for blame; my urge to share my anguish with him; take him for my mark, aim my poisoned words at him. Because that is what I must not do, the ultimate madness. I had been festering for so long—I mustn't infect him too, ask him to justify himself, accuse him of my sins: 'Am I your shit then, that you let me fall into the Mad Bed?' As if I had committed my sins for him, so he could fling me away from him, disown me because of my sickness, as if I had caught it for him, so he could raise a fence round the bed where the whore had me cornered. I longed to call him so he could show me my degradation. I longed to disgust him, so that he could forgive me. I needed to hurt him as much as possible, so that he would know himself by my crimes. Say to him: 'Am I not the prodigal daughter returning to you in delusion and lies, in a monster's gown, so you can dredge me up from your memory?' Because I was afraid to speak to him. Afraid he would guess my iniquity. Because I despaired. Because I hoped he would relieve me; let me off; lead me at last to my end. Covered with shame and hatred. At the feet of my judge.

What binds you to him? Loss of Memory. Such a load of fears and aberrations. Empty double beds where you dare not go to sleep because the sheets are made of steel. If there is a phone it has been cut off. Who disconnected it? The temptation to warn the man who is your mother that you are going to betray him; get the wrong person; get the wrong number. A woman's voice answers. It was death. I was certain. How could I have avoided it in my anguish? Ask the impossible in an icy voice: 'Could I speak to God?'—'Who's speaking?' Good question. I scarcely understood the words that came out of my body. My real tongue did not move. I opened my sex—words cold as snakes. 'Give me God. It's urgent. A question of deception.' That voice, not his. It was his wife's voice. I was so weak and crazed, no strength left to be surprised or even anxious; anxiety would come later. If you phone god in a moment of Forgetfulness, because night won't go by, not knowing who you are, and if you come upon your death in person, don't think about it, you were not born to accuse but to be judged. Betrayal for betrayal. Insist. 'May I please . . .' I repeated. Who told you it's his wife? Such a craving for suffering! For believing you don't believe. Everything depends on his story; on doing what you must not do. So you can tell him on the phone, in a state of terror: 'I've done it.' Say it to him and swear to it. You should have hung up; lied to tell the truth; backed down. That way you could have Forgotten again. You could have succeeded in thinking you were his monster. 'I've done it.' His silence on the phone. As if I had killed my mother. 'I've done it, done it.' Do I even know what? Where? Why? How? His silence doesn't believe me.—Why did I do it? I don't know. Because you wanted me to. Because I was mad. To obey. To deserve your disgust. To

79

get him back to me. In case of Amnesia: so that he knows me by my faults.

I had been missing him for so long. I needed him to miss me. He missed me in the Wrong Bed. The real reason why I relieved myself in suffering and heresy—I myself have Forgotten.

Who let me run off in the wrong direction? Waste my days in cities like forests? Get the wrong life, three times? Who let me go out of my mind at ten o'clock, the back way? And I had a date at ten o'clock with the man who keeps my death away. He came, I'm sure. It's not love that makes you come screaming back to him, it's Guilt! Your judge was there. Why didn't you leave a message for him at your mother's? He would have waited at first. As before. Did you leave any doubts lying around? Ambivalence? I ran along accusing myself, the interrogation gripping me, the city streets had emptied; I was chasing through the streets in anguish, in broad daylight, life laid bare, my sight was returning. Compromising documents? Letters? Petty infidelities? What a lot of charges against you! What have you to say in reply? Nothing? The truth: You forgot, and went out. It was so long since you'd seen him. It was a summer's day. A quarter of an hour. A lifetime to go wrong in. My eyes, groping, looking, trying to bore through space—went astray. 'It will serve you right if you never set eyes on him again.' I was attacking myself. The living had disappeared behind closed windows. 'It was summer. Time has broken down. I had been waiting so long for him.' The city emptied, as if everything had been spewed up. I was running along, preparing to try and defend myself. Not easy with all those shadows accusing me, those bastards crowding round me, monsters, lion-dragons, the hookers I had engendered more or less consciously. I was wearing myself out, it was true I was handling things badly, tired of so much ugliness and opposition, but I was desperately anxious to get my words in: a few words, a prayer, not even a prayer, a final affirmation, that's all I asked; just permission, before the end, to tell the Saintly Breast the other truth, the one that had cost us so many human lives, so much cherished blood, spilled, drunk, spat out. Only three words, the only ones to survive—that was the proof—all the others were repressed, only these words rescued. In these circumstances the difficulty was almost insuperable, but I had enough breath left, enough strength, enough love of truth to be able to throw out this 'I love you'. At that moment someone shouted: 'Well? Have you finished? How much longer is this farce going on for?'

As if someone had read my thoughts. 'And so, you wait a few minutes and no longer? A little absence and presence (of mind) goes? You can't hold out any longer? It was easy to blame me. My faults were piling up so fast. I was adding to them all the time. Who will avenge the man with the smile better than I who live only to pay for him? Purging love to throw it away with the blood that purified it.

—'Why are you accusing me? I'm coming! Hold on to him! Stop him! It's a question of madness!'

I had such an urgent need to be judged! To be blamed by him. If he were there, let him be stern. Hopelessly cool and cold. So that I could be finally condemned. Rest. Blame him for being cool. Cold. Iniquitous.

—'What do you have to say?'—Eleven o'clock. Nothing. Not even a lie. No help. You who wouldn't have gone away from him for a second. Nor even pretended. You were deluded.

No reason. Except a crazy: 'As if nothing, as if no one, as if never.' If you didn't exist; if I'd never been born. To lose you. No reason: not even to forget him. To get myself wrong, the world wrong, the street wrong; to be wronged, by the world, by memory. As if I didn't exist for myself. You are the victim of a delusion: you sleep, go out, when you get back it is so dark, the watch has stopped, the beds are empty, no one to ask—you are so frightened to come back into another body, it's better not to wake yourself up. You dawdle along, roam around, can't go on any longer. Who will re-call me? Who will bring me back to someone? Night was at a standstill. The terrors arrived. They stopped time. While I wasn't myself. No one to wake me up, my memory had been disconnected. I so wanted to know who loved me; whom I loved more than myself. I wanted to know at which judge's feet to throw myself, to be pardoned for treason. To weep. Tell him the whole other truth. Hold him back for a minute. A second. Only an illusion. The time it takes for me to come back to myself.

Someone wants me to lose my head. They are trying to trap me. Bring me down. They won't tell me my name to help me come back to myself; help me complain to the proper quarter. I began to yell with all my strength. 'Call me! I'm coming! It's a question of names. I am ready to confess everything! I am coming back to be condemned!' It was a brighter day than usual. The streets hardly moved at all though I was running like the wind. Someone was sending me a bad dream. A staggeringly brutal incident occurred. Two phoney seers passed me. Two young, confident men dressed like lion-dragons. They had men's eyes but they looked at me like monsters. The streets reared up under their feet, I was almost knocked down. They were pushing a child in front of them. A stranger. I was convinced I had seen him before. In the daylight he had the same look—I was sure I remembered—as I had had when I had seen the Great Saint in person staring at me without seeing me. Because of desertion. They were setting up an execution. Everything was going so fast, so smoothly I was paralysed with amazement. An inexorable machine. Straight ahead, two steps away. It was going on before my eyes. They measured the little child from head to waist, waist to feet. Impossible to make a sound. They cut him a death-pattern out of steel paper. I stayed where I was for a moment, unable to look again, overcome with dread. I have felt like that before. I just managed to keep my head. It was an illusion. They laid him down on a plank of white wood. His head was pale and sad. If I hadn't thought that all this was just a dream I would have shrieked in terror. All this was just a rare kind of dream imposed on me, a dream someone was administering to me to drive me crazy; to stop me. A lying vision to make me lose my head. They really wanted me to Forget. I tore myself away. I went home. The moment I disappeared, trembling, as I was still in the yard, in front of the door, the execution took place. The phoney seers were commenting on it; I was too far away to see, too near to miss what they were saying. The scene was well ordered, each phase clearly reported: the setting up of the machine, the explanation of how it worked, its starting, then the execution: the corpse, cut in two, rolled onto the large sheets of paper. I began to howl as loud as I could. I was in bed with the wolf-dragon. I was asleep. The Monster was giving me this dream. Or else it was my Fault. My limbs were paralysed. I wanted at all costs to pull down my paper-gown which was tucked up, but my hands didn't obey. The wolf-dragon's feet on my buttocks. I was screaming, suffering like Mad.

Things were going on behind my eyes. Impossible to shut them. My soul tossing about, I saw myself convulsed with sobs, unable to get back, unable to prevent the situation. Oh! Oh! I was screaming myself hoarse. Oh! Oh! Have pity. Unable to get out, escape, be woken up. The phoney seers held me in their claws, tore at my arms with their talons like eagles' beaks. They were telling me their lies. 'You brought yourself to death with your phoney lamb's ways. No use denying it. We knew you by your dreams.'

How could I have taken another step? Until the man with the Breast took my dreams away, I was surrounded by unreal visions. I was writhing in fear on the pavement, until he came and fetched me in the dark. If only he would take me in his arms of memory, clasp me to his huge, tender chest, offer me his big loving penis in the night. And his penis was big and strong and blue in the dark, like a day dawning, and I clung to it, suffocating; I hung on to it and remembered with certainty that the penis he was offering me was the same as god the mother's, forgotten so long ago, taken away from me so long ago—the real day was about to dawn: you were going to wake up to yourself. Get up shivering with fright. I was saved. Hurry to the man whom you had forgotten to think about at ten o'clock. Tell him, as soon as you're up. Ask him to explain. Who made this Blank in my memory? As soon as this dream is over. But he couldn't know the truth, the murder, the horror which was taking place so near us in the dark, which I couldn't stop. And, clutching the penis, I went on screaming till the body was cut in two. In the street. No one went by.

How can you not forget? How can you want to remember? No explanation. Except the worst. Someone wants me to murder him. I didn't dare accuse anyone. I had been deserted so often before. Two steps away from myself, forever. In the gardens beside the houses I could no longer enter. Because of the beds I collapsed in. Parted so often from the body I was clinging to. What have I done to you that you hate me like death? Didn't I forget you so you could judge me?—How many times?—Three or four. To vindicate your harshness. I lay down in the wrong bed to prove you right. I behaved like a substitute sheep. While I was convulsed with fright a scaffold was set up in the yard in front of my house. Who is forcing me to die in the night? To chase after bodies for weeks on end without managing to stay my hunger? *You* don't forget. It's *love* that takes fright, thinking it has been forgotten. Love is drunk with dread, tricked, tripped, put to bed between sheets of pain, made to dream cruel dreams. Love is woken up one minute too late. They do everything to drive love mad. While you thought you were sleeping they are preparing your

84

execution. You are being deceived, a memory Lapse is keeping you in a treacherous bed; they swear you are dreaming, that you can sleep, that, the stranger is being judged, not you. Who is splitting me in two? Who is making me believe I am dreaming even when I am awake? Time, truth are hidden from me. The points are disconnected. Anti-memory screens everywhere. The fake prophets are asking you in their siren voices to stay lying down: 'Enjoy yourself, don't move, the Great Saint will come and save you.' They assure you that you are not asleep. How can you stop yourself listening to them? Their loving tone, their old wives' tales, their messages of paradise? And no one to call me back. My memory had been disconnected. My soul plugged in to treachery. Their gentle looks: 'Sleep my child, you are not asleep. You can go to sleep without worrying.' Asleep, I thought I was sleeping, I was sure I was awake, the scaffold in the yard hadn't been set up for me, I still had a head on my shoulders, eyes open, I trusted.

In the dark I wondered whether I wasn't being tricked by Amnesia, whose point of view I did not trust. No one answered me. The phoney seers reassured me. The monster had unreal visions in store for me. I was lying in fine sheets which hid time from me—it was always the same time.

There are some rooms which you can't leave without losing your reason. 'Stay where you are.' I wanted to get up. Sleep weighed so heavy on me. Someone was going to be killed in the yard. Who has to die? An old woman was lecturing me: 'It's an optical illusion. Your scaffold is only a table. They are getting breakfast ready. You can go to sleep. Beware of your suspicions which make you believe lies and undermine your craving for peace.' I didn't recognize her, but that didn't frighten me. I was thinking while she tucked me in again: 'If she were a phoney grand-mother I'd feel I knew her.' I felt I was wrong, but I didn't know what about. Probably a question of words. I didn't dare say anything to the old woman. If she was wicked she would be powerful. My thoughts came and went, more and more confused, each one urging me to do what I ought to have done. The atmosphere was electric. Phone? Who? The stranger. To find out what was going on. Why I was letting myself lie in a room where people I loathed were sneaking in. I tried to dial the number. I sat on the Monster's lap, leaning against her dugs. There was no justification for that position except the general upset and the events which were about to take place in front of my door. The old woman was saying to me: 'No one is in danger. The yard is empty. You must have re-read *The Trial*.' The phone wasn't working. Two harpies came into the yard—I didn't know *who* I would be any more. They were two monstrous cops. I was so overwrought I could see them from the window through the closed windows. If someone was being murdered I was sure I would understand. I had suffered that torture before. The tragic thing was the lack of communication. The stranger was careful not to spread the news. The news wouldn't have been true. No one would have heard.

The streets had emptied. 'No use going out. It's a mock-execution.' In such cases you dare not Remember any more, out of compassion for the victim; and a hint of antipathy. Go back to sleep because you are powerless; to avoid being a conscious accomplice; don't move an inch, to avoid precipi-tating the events which you want to witness; unconsciously. 'What's the good of torturing yourself? You have read this story several times before.' But I had forgotten the details. If it was a question of murder you had to be on the alert. I did so want to know what was going on. My memory was deceiving me: instead of sending the whole scene back to me in one, it was giving it to me in bits and pieces. I was guessing, frightened, I couldn't quite make out the person concerned. The end was hidden from me. 'And then? Afterwards?' The business was being played back to me the wrong way round—I had no proof, except my anguish. In the room things were going on between grand-mother and I. I was five years old, grandmother was a seer. I was sitting on her lap, she was telling me the story of the Big Bad Wolf. I saw her mouth contort. If I had been her Little Red Riding Hood I would have yelled. Gripped by hatred and shame I looked at her face in profile, her fierce look. One way or another I was lost. I didn't dare escape. Grand-mother turned her old hypocrite face to me and told me to take care: 'There will be widespread Famine.' I plunged into oblivion. I never knew the ending. But I felt the truth. The Monster said to me: 'That scene is a farce. The trial has already taken place. Last year. On a certain date.' The Monster spoke with an Austrian accent, all the words were distorted. In the house between K and the nurse of the dead. What's the good of whimpering, despite myself, I was K and I had been put on the nurse's lap—she was just like the wolf-dragon. I said to myself: the story is beginning all over again in reverse. In the other book she was on me. I clung to that distinction. To gain time. As long as I pretended to believe the tale things wouldn't proceed, the end would be postponed.

I was taking a chance, hoping to wake up before it was revealed to me. It cost me dear, it was really risky, no guarantee. Leap first—look afterwards! Sitting on the nurse's lap, (half-male, half mortal), and me in my little vice-gown, (half dead, half-female), letting her caress me, hoping that the night would come to an end before the story ended. Not knowing what would happen; what had happened already; if the story had a happy ending; what end was reserved for me . . . such a longing to get out! Between her legs, helpless, not protesting, not knowing what I was trying to avoid, paying in advance just in case, pretending to be her Little Lamb, not naughty but a bit of a hypocrite. She called me her naughty little child. I pretended to be what she wanted. What's the good of protecting myself against the nurse, since I didn't know who I would possibly be if I managed to get up; I had no one else to hide; even if I hadn't pretended nothing would have changed. While it was all beginning all over again I really was her naughty little child: none other than the victim of the nurse of dead children. If I managed to escape before she carried out her plan I would remember myself; if I got out alive I would know myself by my lies and feigned enjoyment. I let her lick me without crying out: as long as her tongue was running over me the end was postponed. Eyes shut. To avoid seeing her heavy body, the wolf-dragon features under her nurse's clothes, her men's legs and her feet in shoes ripped by her claws. Pretend not to feel her tongue climbing up your back, her clawless hands on your buttocks, her big predatory breasts at your back. Sitting on her lap, her fig-wood, don't look at her sex organs shaped like fingers, with the eyes of a woman at their tips. And when one of the mouths of this half-female nurse reaches your chest, after hundreds of attempts, just when you think a real day may be dawning, night is going to end, no point in struggling, if after thousands of detours that mouth comes to rest on your breast, where you weren't expecting it—before that moment you didn't even know you had breasts—what's the use of being suspicious of that mouth. Her tongues circle round your breast, her snakes on your skin, her dogs are going to bite their lord and master with their amorous teeth—you would be struggling in vain. Night will have it's way—no one to tell you off. Because I tried to put off the end, while I was on her lap my suspicions were lulled by death, whose mouth poured out all its desires and heresies over my breast. I could have tried to defend myself but its desires penetrated my breast, the heresy entered my bones; my reason toppled. I was five years older. I didn't feel any pain. My breast began to swell. What's wrong with that? No pain, the breast was taking its pleasure under the wolf-dragon's thick lips. Terrified I watched it grow bigger, its pleasure spilling over; I watched it go wild, struggling like a horse trying to throw its rider. I was paralysed with fright. The breast had broken loose, it was only just holding on. I did so long to get the thing over with; pretend not to notice anything; let the breast decide. I didn't want to see the wolf-

88

dragon break loose, run all over my earth-mother body, go out of my yard into the streets; I didn't want to feel it hanging round its master like a mad man, piercing my feet with its fangs as it spewed out its honeyed madness into my wounds. I wanted a taste of its heresy, a feel of its insanity. Without fainting. Let its blasphemy pierce to the quick, trick my organs and tangle my nerves like the Big Bad Wolf's tangled mane. Let it fulfil its desires without collapsing; I wanted the strength, the shame, the courage to let its pleasure continue until the breast had discharged its poison. I wanted its reckless anguish without denying my suffering, without disguising that I was trembling with grief, afraid of the Great Saint's anger, if he came to surprise me in my sleep and found me sitting an the Monster's lap. Her thighs were stuck together, the wood not cut, impossible to contemplate her genital organs. She will not be known by her fruits but by the image of madness she reflects. But when the breast was erect, just when it was about to rush off, the telephone boomed. I lifted the receiver. If someone had called me I might hear the voice of a real mother. Hallo? Hallo? The voice of the man with the real breast. His angry voice. No one. Love had been cut off. His silence was screaming at me. I was sure it was him. You were sleeping! No offence meant. And what if you hadn't been phoned? Stopped? Before the crime was committed? Now I felt that I had always known that I wouldn't find out the end. One minute before, the telephone. An extremely important voice. I wouldn't have lain down in anguish, I wouldn't have been so far away, if I had known *who* I would be before I faced death. I would have got up, run out without asking my way. It isn't worth phoning the stranger. But I did wonder who would get out. It seemed someone wanted me to murder him. The machine was already being set up in the yard. I was sure they were waiting for me. That's why I delayed. I was afraid to be condemned.

They want me to know my crimes by the tortures I suffered. I am not sitting on death's lap without waking up in order to forget you. But so that I can pretend my sufferings are not real.

Am I guilty because I slept so long? Wasn't I right to hide away in sleep, not to rest, but to bury with me the grave anxieties that are wearing me out? Right to go down into the dark with all my creatures and all the monsters created to stop me getting out? I am so afraid that if I make a move I will fall into the monster's clutches; if I go forwards I'll step on a lion-dragon's tail, offend a monster as I back away. Afraid of being accused—how could I not confess?—afraid of being judged, afraid that two harpies with blazing eyes will drag me away from the house where I have an appointment with god the mother.

The telephone rang. I was afraid to lift the receiver. It wasn't the real phone, more like an alarm bell. Get out no matter how. What if they woke me up—guilty. That would be a dangerous awakening. Lift up the steel sheets: my trapped part trying to escape; overcome with shame and regret. Dreams were tormenting me. 'Wake up. Life will begin without you.' Dreams pulled me out of bed, half alseep. Dragged me across the room into chaos. Things were overturned, turned against me, growling, punishing me, doing their best to upset me. Through the chaos. And it was one of the worst places I had ever woken up in, too late.

What's the good of waking up? Answering the summons? When it is always too late. Treacherous dreams led me astray. They came to me in the form of passageways: 'Come along us, this way, you will wake up much sooner.' I followed them. The house was heaving, rooms exploding in chaos, because of me of course—but not only because of me: the walls were turning black as I was struggling in the passageways against the furniture which had turned into beasts. When I reached the ante-room it was past ten. Hours had gone by. Chaos all round me. Another room to get through. Then I would be in the Living room. Over there on the other side. The man with the Breast will question me! Cool, cold: at last, tell everything, at last. With no explanation. To be judged harshly! The ante-room was cluttered: card-board boxes everywhere, mattresses, pillows, incriminating evidence, all the beds to bear witness. The space was swarming with crowds coming in and out and examining. I had come to the end of the world. No going back. There is nothing after that. All the phoney seers in this dead-end were huddled together and the fake grand-mothers, whom I hadn't dared offend. Is there a little empty patch left anywhere in the universe where I could be buried if I were put to death? One little square yard where no one would touch me? A miniature paradise, where I can be forgotten, alone? I was sweating, suffocating. A very faint breath of air reached me from the great Saint. Like a remembrance of trust; a sweet scent despite the stinking crowds. It reminds me that life is still there outside, two or three steps away. You remember that reality exists. Even if you can't reach it. Even though it is so near. The important thing is that it exists. One single tree at the end of the earth and you can breathe again!

What would he say? If he came? Too late. Who is guilty? If it's me isn't it him? I was anxious on his behalf. Who let anguish win the battle I fought last night while asleep? Who let me come to the entrance of the Living room in this indecent state, with no shoes on, dirty feet, half-dressed and besides, my head not very firmly on my shoulders? 'I am unclean, I am broken. But love is fixed in my heart forever.' The interrogation had begun at ten o'clock precisely. How to reply? My tongue didn't loosen up. Upset, I must have taken the wrong one. Instead of speaking it was foaming dangerously. Faulty connection. What if it were going to explode? No time to tear the plug out and replace it; it takes hours to repair. If only I could have talked to him!

Nothing to say. I've lost my chance. If only I could see him standing, even in a dream, through my panic and shame, my

91

crimes, armed troops, through dim memories, walls, behind screens, bars; if only I could wake up for one second and see him through my tears—one second too late.

In the Living room the table was laid. I came before this altar in my sheep's gown, barefoot, not awake. The altar was well furnished: knives, chopping blocks, electric grinders. As if the judge had laid out all this apparatus for show. Is it his fault? It was mine. Instead of getting the breakfast you were wallowing in your Loss. 'It's my fault. I'm sorry. If there is any guilt around it's mine—again. I am known in advance by my passion.'

No use excusing yourself. Yesterday and today it was written.

—'What do you have to say against yourself?'

A (death) sentence arrived. I thought it was for me. All I did was kill myself. I was tricked by the Pangs of Anguish. They just walked straight back in.

I was lying down in the back room. No time to save myself. Time had just stopped. I knew I was lost before the Pangs began. They could read my thoughts, predict what I feared. Their strange look annoyed me: they looked meek as mice but underneath they were cats. I was expecting what they told me. The same old treachery. They told me what I was thinking. As effective as ever. As if you believed what you thought! They pretended to question me.

—Who do you love? Who is not here? What chance have you lost?

As if they didn't know. You yourself don't remember. Like a machine to drive you to despair. You can't stop it by yourself. You needed the great Saint to come and switch it off. He alone and no one else—because he couldn't come. When did you forget him? Lose him? For how long?—their poisonous questions disguised in sugary answers. I understood the moment I heard their voices, causing a breakdown in communication without seeming to interfere. Round my bed, their faces like Big Bad Mothers disgusted me, interested me;

were constantly changing. They began to shake up my love to test it. And I did the same too, to see if it held together. They pretended to be worried. Why did he let you sleep? And now you have no one to re-call you to yourself. He could have warned you. Sent you some memories. If he knew of your unhappiness. How could he not know? If he loved you, he would know what was going on. Who cut you off? You wouldn't have done it yourself. The investigation seemed to be making progress, they hemmed in my reason. The Pangs of Anguish clutched at my arms with their men's hands, shook me like a fruit-tree to see if it was well stocked. And I did the same to my soul too, to test its powers of resistance. They anticipated my treacherous desires with their phoney questions. Who was he? He doesn't seem to be here any more. Are you sure he was here? Can you prove it? You can't prove it any longer. You believed in paradise—because you wished to lose it. There never was a paradise. Am I wrong? You know you have always known. But I didn't know. My face grey, not answering, wanting to get angry. I detested these Pangs, their old tricks, treacherous kisses, their self-satisfaction. And they'd just walked in unannounced to frustrate my desires. Don't you really want what you pretend *not* to want? How could I resist? I no longer knew what I did want. I didn't know whom I distrusted. Their questions to find out how far I had gone wrong, lurking in all the passage-ways of my dreams, pierced me. I watched them go by unconcerned: their fat heads big with monstrous answers; foreheads bulging with lies, the old cows incensed me. I knew what they were chewing over. No use protesting. If I'd attacked them I knew they'd have spat out their abortions all over me. Better not annoy them. They'll end up going away. When all your fears have come true.

Why deny it? You have been heard dreaming. You don't believe it any more. You were mistaken. You were telling yourself a fairy-tale. You didn't even believe it yourself.

The kind of tale you tell yourself so that you are only half-deceived; to slow things down, beat your guilt. I could guess the author by the pain the story caused me. I was sad before it began. It happened in my room. A letter was asking me:

'Why search for the missing man? Do you really think you'll find him again? —*I* don't think so. But *love* does.' Faith can work miracles. The room was stifling. All the tears that had been shed formed a thick, heavy mist. To search for him you had to brush aside these invisible curtains continuously. I did all that love demanded. I wept. I lifted up the damp curtains which flopped to the ground like the dead weight of a huge body which will never wake again. I crawled into all the corners where he could have crept in, if he had been hiding to frighten us. I could feel the story's impatience. And I wasn't moving so slowly because I had no strength left, or was unwilling, but because of love, yes, I wanted to be merciful, just in case. Because he was still alive: as long as I went on searching for him he was still alive. I was giving him all the chances he needed. Besides, the dampness, darkness, the mounting tension in the air and the fading light which could hardly penetrate made each gesture slower and more solemn. How could I blame the story for not helping me? Blame love for exhausting me? After all, it was the Saintly Breast who was paralysing us. If the room had been the size of a castle I would have spent years struggling. I wouldn't have been daunted by the prospect of spending the best part of my life there. I could have worked faster, the magnitude of the task would have inspired another sort of courage. At the heart of my sad toil a certain joy would have been possible: in the end *I* might have died without ever having lost *him*—even if I had never found him again. But it was a small room. Much too small to contain such extraordinary events. So cramped and confined that at times, as I forced open small pieces of furniture, went through a drawer without believing I'd find him—my fingers limp with unhappiness—I had the feeling that I had used up this meagre space and that I was plunging my hands into the flesh of the man with the Breast. A terrifying feeling,

obviously an illusion. I explored everything humanly possible.
Where he could be hidden, if he were very small, where he
could be found. Where I could not have found him. I
persisted in looking where it would have been impossible for a
human being to hide. I also searched where it would have
been impossible to find him alive—if he were a human being,
but not if he were a god. In the bookshelves in the bookcase,
on the table, I turned envelopes, pillow cases inside out,
turned out everything that can be turned inside out, I turned
my eyes inside out—to see what a human being cannot
possibly see. To find what keeps on disappearing, forcing you
to go on searching for it; what is hidden yet not lost. To find
what affectionate human beings are forbidden to re-call by a
name, a face or the gradual fading of a pain—but seers may.

You listen to books lying on their backs complaining that
they are open for such a long time and in the end they are not
touched, fingered; complaining that they have been written
for no one, begun and then dropped in the middle. You hear
their voices protesting like wounded nymphs: 'Why wake us
up, why undress us, why ask us to yield the secrets of
immortality and then drop us on the table, before we can
express ourselves?'—and you can't give them the attention
they deserve; can't benefit from their tenderness, experience
and generosity. Respectfully, you refuse to argue with their
text, 'the one I am searching for is not there; hasn't come yet;
hasn't been announced yet; caught in a book; captured by a
symbol'—you close them. 'Go to sleep. Don't torture
yourself. The missing man can't have been written yet.' The
room was making incredible suggestions to me: 'Probe my
walls, my loins, the important thing is to go on searching'
through messages on the radio, through analogy, through
thought association. I felt a certain resistance, I disliked the
impossible, but I obeyed because love demanded it; the Pangs
of Anguish were gratified. I re-read (with no faith in it) the
anonymous Promissory Letter which was lying around on the
desk: 'You will find him again, or you won't.' Unable to

interpret it you read it a hundred times, uncertain whether it was addressed to you. Sometimes it promises you 'You will find him or you won't'; sometimes it drives you to despair; reassures you; you change your mind, you will never find him—that's really what you wanted isn't it? As long as you haven't found him it is impossible to lose him, impossible to know what you would have lost—go on looking and hoping. The room was minute? I only hope there is no time limit: it's not space that counts it's time. To have all the time you need not to find him. No one else in the room but you . . . I wouldn't have written this story like that—And when love, almost invisible in the dark, asked me to search in the bed, between the folds of the leaden sheets, who could blame it? Hate was the one who made the decision. I couldn't suppress bitter tears. 'Not there! I begged. 'Not yet.' If he were between the sheets he would be dead. 'Let's look under the bed,' I said. He couldn't be there; he would have to be as thin as a sheet of paper to creep under there; but if he had managed to, he would be found alive. The air circulating at floor level was thick but breathable; flat on my belly, hardly thicker than a paper-knife, I crawled under the crushing vault of the bed—while human love faded away into the night, as the author had prescribed. As if he had half-read the Promissory Letter from the writer's point of view: 'You will not find him.' It was a letter of Conviction. I wouldn't have taken it like that. It was being read to me in the dark, from the end of the world.

You could tell death's style by the pretence at hesitation, the detours, the obstacles to be overcome, by the obvious, hopelessly tortuous narrative tricks. I had the terrifying feeling that death was telling me this story it had written specially for me. Death must have seen itself in my dreams and my suffering and now hoped to dictate to me all the

96

stories that I wanted to write for love. Yet another of those lies that we are only too eager to half-believe; to deceive the Pangs of Anguish when they are stronger than we are. All the abortive stories: corpses of stories; interrupted stories; unfinished stories—because there is never any one left to finish them, to produce the book of death.

You should beware when a letter from death is addressed to you. It's a forgery. If you weren't there to read it it couldn't come. It would never have been sent off. I could never read a story like that. I was weak. It was read to me by force. I struggled. I didn't believe it at all, but I was suffering desperately, as if *I* had dictated it.

I didn't write it. I would have written it differently. In the state I was in, crushed under the weight of the sheets, watched by the Pangs of Anguish who were ten times more powerful than I, better armed, better at resisting, I had little chance of escaping it. I imagined how I would have read the story if I could have got the upper hand. Grab hold of the letter; dictate the right way to read it or tear it up. Letters have nothing to say to you; it's your decision. My will must have been disconnected. Impossible to impose the reading I'd set my heart on. I longed to turn the page. Nothing to be done. Dead hands, numb fingers, useless arms, this body is out of order. I could see the other story beginning on another page. All that was needed was a slight movement of the wrist; a transition phrase. I was held back by a feeling of powerlessness whose power amazed me. The Voice of Weariness was imploring me to stop wanting; imploring me to be half-deceived, to day-dream of escape; to make up stories that don't end in blood, loneliness, resignation; stories that go on, refusing to be interrupted, thrown back into the past, lead to cells where they die out, dragged into blind-alleys and knocked senseless, cut to pieces and their corpses thrown as

97

food for anguish—Death takes all the royalties and I take the rights to suffering, and lose my head—stories which don't allow themselves to be mutilated, muzzled, forced to commit suicide; I wanted stories that are not convinced that everything has already been written before they began with a forged letter signed: 'Lost.'

My Weariness was giving me advice: 'What's the use of making up stories which take off since there will be no one to read them on the other side—if there is another side—no one to carry them on. You'd better make the best of it: sleep, don't dream, make peace with anguish.' There was good sense in this down to earth advice; the low voice to which I was not insensible was seductive. Die a little, let yourself be coached, affected by the bass voice with its husky hoarse tone, its insistence, its winning helplessness, its powerful weariness that infects you with its mildness, attracts you, makes you want to give in, relax. A little laziness and indolence, a small dose of cowardice. Weariness taking me in hand. A slight pain in the head, an ache which is vaguely pressing. My body had something serious to say. I listened to its mysterious precision. I was in pain and the pain was precious to me. A headache of this kind is all or nothing. If it stays in the head it's just an idea. If it gets into the marrow you've got it: the sickness is incurable. What is happening in your body? What secret has it been chosen to bear? No need for a doctor to guess. Death has laid hands on you. Joy! Isn't that why your head was on fire? At last you have the sickness that no one dares hope for. The great disease that cures those in anguish. You can leave it to the disease without worrying. It will willingly lead you to the goal that you didn't dare face: 'The fatal sickness!' My weariness welcomed it. 'At last! like a signature to your books! One last page and it will all be over.'

This weariness had a curious look which wouldn't let me rest. Something insidious in its face—I had seen that look before. I must have looked like that the day I received my first Conviction.

*

When my first Conviction came I was lying in the back room.
I wasn't writing at the time. The stories which came weren't
fairy-tales, they were more or less true. My body was living
them. Everything happened as if in reality. Things were
announced on the phone and the radio, I was reading the text
on Parting, the one I never could read through to the end.
When Tristan turned his face to the wall I was overwhelmed
with grief, the book fell from my hands, I turned my face to
the wall and wept. The story was interrupted; I would have
written it differently. 'Wait. Give me time,' I begged. 'I'm
with you in spirit! Wait a minute! Let me try!' Why interrupt
the book? Do you really think you can change what has
already been done? I didn't *think* anything, I *wished*. Love
needed to. If life wanted to, it was up to me to sort it out. What
would I have lived on if love had been killed? Face to the wall,
I wept, I didn't write, the beloved was not dying, life didn't
come but death was kept off. With all my dreams to help me I
tried to create another scene for love, ignoring the laws, not
believing in it, yet unable to stop myself from racking my soul.
All my tears and anger turned to a few grains of sand and a
little light—enough to sketch another space from which I
could make up a better story. I felt I had been born to stop
love dying: so that I wouldn't die before I had saved them.
While she wasn't there, love turned to the wall, wishing to die.
And I held it back with prayers and promises, I kept it alive
by keeping it in sight. I tried with the help of all my visions to
draw the flickering image which would make it possible to
overcome separation. I tried to change the wall into a screen
on which a fair-way for love could be projected.

That was the night of my last hope. My faith almost
exhausted. The next day I would have ceased to believe. I
have noticed it happening before: the moment you give up
you are granted what you had stopped waiting for. For

example: when god the mother only revealed herself to me face to face when I had begun to tell myself that god didn't exist after all. Paradise is not lost; you just find it too late. When you have stopped imagining it. Then you see god coming, in reality, you recognize him for certain by his quick light step, his smile; as if he had waited for the second when you have lost faith to reveal himself to you. After that your faith will never be the same again. I was reading *Tristan and Yseult* for the hundredth and last time. I was hopeless. I would give them up to their fate. Too tired to persist in trying to change the story. I would never read the end, I could guess it only too well; it had been written by death, to spite me. The moment I gave up I had a vision.

They are an admirable couple. If they are alive everything is possible. I watched them from afar. I didn't want to let go of them. I wanted to keep their bodies through the strength of my love. I had never succeeded in creating two such adorable beings before. They were living. A man, a woman, the man and the woman one for the other, love, the unique light. Separate, different, one body seemed slightly more feminine, perhaps the other body more masculine, but I wasn't sure about anything, a feminine man, a woman—life personnified. And they wanted to live differently. They wouldn't be easily destroyed. It was still in the Middle Ages. Their beauty could but be intolerable. Premature. Tomorrow's love. The world would do all it could to destroy them. They would set out, nothing would stop them. What's the good of burying yourself in the dark tunnel that still serves as our universe, living the life of a worm? I decided to do all I could to free them. They were being watched. The tunnel was swarming with people who hated them. Not only the police but the whole of society, all its hypocritical jealous men and women. I projected them outside in one go. Two thunderclaps. Saved. As soon as they were in the darkness there was a commotion while I invented their flight. A prisoner of these dark times, in the midst of preparations for repression, I played the fool as if I had nothing to do with them. I played the idiot while troops were massing at the openings, ridiculous armies with cross-bows which could nevertheless kill if you came within reach. I turned base and mediocre like them, in order to invent in secret, beings who are not tolerated in reality, in order to get near the frontier without being stopped; to back up to the gate, nonchalantly. To send them, in one movement of my soul, living into the light, into eternity. Imagine their journey. Work with feverish brain to give them the means to go where no one has ever been before, alive; get them over the frontiers in a powerful car; once passed the limits of the possible, give them instructions for the future. Bring them to life, lead them, worship them, endow them with energies you yourself don't possess, give them all the virtues you could never have. Follow them to the end—beyond is the other life, to be reached on foot over the mountains which I could see rising up, too steep for me—I watched them tackling them from afar. Now that the alarm had been given it would be difficult for me to escape. But I had only one desire: to join them one day, or never. To live tomorrow or let the past destroy me.

My face turned to the wall, I could see them take the mountains by storm; they were about to see the Promised Life. If you see in a vision two different beings approaching the future with just the right amount of strength and tenderness—the world disappears—their beautiful faces are bent over a face which could be yours if you succeeded in joining them and creating yourself in their image, the gods themselves are going to embrace you, and it will be *the* embrace, the one that takes place at the beginning of the other world.

Instantly the telephone rings. To bring you down. No need to pick up the receiver. You have already heard what death has to say to you. You know the world's hatred.

I had always thought it would end like this. Wasn't I alone, as far away as possible from my family, defenceless, lying down face to the wall, unarmed, incapable of turning the page? And at that time I couldn't write; I didn't even read, my thoughts were read: the books that were writing my story hurt so much that I was overwhelmed before the end. As I listened to them I had the feeling that god was reading my thoughts before I even began to think, live, even before I met him; and everything had been written as truthfully as possible, about *me*. A truth I knew nothing about but which I recognized as the story came to a head, closed in, ran me to earth, propelled me through peoples and centuries; stopping me settling down, staying my hunger, enjoying myself; pulled me out of beds where I was trying to hide and in one defeat after another undeceived me, forced me to despair, at grips with love; forced me to believe only to be betrayed, to pledge myself only to be forced to break my promises, to escape from a trap only to hurl myself into a cage—so that I would come to the end of the world. After I had sincerely tried, terrified, to fit in: to get a place in one of its schools, to get accepted in one of its beds, to get a seat in one of its halls, one of its classes, one of its administrations. Yet I had never managed to be tolerated, employed, given a post, but had always been expelled, spewed up, avoided, forced to compete continually in order to be failed over and over again. You won't get through. You will never be found, accepted, sheltered, never fit in, never be admitted, chosen, nourished, caressed, cleared, understood, used, never ever. In the end I had all the proof I needed to see that every single one of my desires would be successfully thwarted.

If I had read the book of my life I would certainly have been able to prove that it was written by death: starting with my death, going backwards from suffering through absence, right back to the first disappointment. At that time I didn't read myself. But all the books talking to me repeated the same old curse: 'You will have all you have asked for. On the last day.'

If I had been able to see that the books were closer to my truth than I knew, I would have read them through to the end; I would have known what was in store for me. Sorrow would have prevented me from finishing them.

I would have noted the hundred and twenty details which proved undeniably that my attempt to get back to myself would fail successfully. An abortive attempt to escape. You want to escape the aptitude test, you refuse to bury yourself forever in the womb of darkness. All you need do to escape from the tunnel in the middle of the night is to go out the door—And why don't you do anything about it? What's stopping you from saving yourself? A desire which counters yours and is much stronger than your longing. Instead of getting out, try *not* to get back to yourself, work the tensions back to front. Dodge the issue; you would seem to be making sure that your return wasn't a return—and yet you couldn't be blamed for wanting to get out. As if I had wanted to please mother against her will: not leaving her and yet not being left to her. And as I obeyed my impulse and dashed off, moving off towards the light, getting closer to the door, I was probably afraid to find out the truth. What truth? No door. No light. No truth. Afraid to find that all I had lived for was to come to the end of the world, face turned to the blank wall—a stony veil. The wall that prevents you from seeing the man with the smile coming up behind you, the man whose smile you have just ceased to believe in; the man who always arrives just late enough for you to have at least one reason to turn your face to the wall; to give yourself up to death, as if death were the mother whom you have promised to gratify for the last time. At least one excuse. 'I wanted to die in your arms and be buried in the same body as you. Alas! my tomb will be a mother to me, and there'll be no one to tell you.''

If things don't want me to live to see the man whom I really long for coming back, who could blame me for going wrong?

No one has come in time to persuade me not to destroy myself. No sign. No Cautionary Letter. Alone, I wept. So that the tears would dim my sight and I couldn't read the last chapter of the Book of Parting. My story would end and I would never know whose fault it was that, when my death sentence was announced I fell in with the decision instead of resisting. If I let myself be put to death it's to honour you, my love. My evasions have not failed: I avoided exemption from punishment. I surrendered to the authorities in the halls of judgement, without arms, without understanding. So my surrender is not a real surrender and yet is considered to be one by the administration. To give anguish complete satisfaction.

There is a murder for you. A corpse is coming back to you and you are still implicated; you are still being pursued. Quite determined not to let yourself be arrested. How hard it is to run through the inner city not returning to the main buildings where trials which you have never yet faced await you. You are afraid to discover the secret; in the courtyard the pulsating bell-towers, the special peaks with divine snow on their summits—like the cities of Anti-Hell are said to look—and the surrounding wall is like god the mother's entrails—but you won't let yourself be caught in that trap! How hard it is to run through the outer city, suffering and indignant, not knowing what is in your dossier, even if, by splitting off and running away, your body has grown and gained in suppleness. It is hard to run fast enough not to be stared at, hard to manage to get out of the capital by a superhuman effort, only to find that the difficulties have not diminished, the chase continues. Your body feels more and more strange, your blood has changed, you have lost the old blood and don't know where the new blood's to come from. The obstacles have changed their nature, bloodless, you now have to plunge into the stifling, dense forest and this makes

104

you more anguished because it is so close, crushing you. You have the feeling you are going to come out in a dead-end somewhere—just a feeling. Go on, further in. There is something fine in the story of your flight, something that you detest, perhaps it's to do with not knowing how all this will end. You don't know the kind of nature you are plunging into, there is something fine that frightens you; now you feel that you have always been running away from it; you don't know what it is, something you have always been trying to get near; that is forcing you to turn into god knows what kind of beast—and you no longer know what kinship to claim; you are forced to run more and more wildly, as if you were running away from your past, afraid of losing it, of finding it, of finding yourself lost in it all over again—running to get closer to it—and while you plunge into the unknown the smell of blood gets stronger, and you start to think that the forest is going to lead you back to a bed which you are dying to reach. You feel you are going to know what bed it is; the scent of blood comes back to you: you seem to have fallen into this bed before, in the other stories. And you are hoping desperately that you will never ever find yourself trapped there again, even in memory.

As soon as the telephone rang out I knew. I was in the back-room. It was the last room in the world. At that time the stories that came were telling me anything they liked. I believed anything because I had stopped believing myself. Lying down, defenceless, with no paper. With no cure powerful enough to keep me alive. And yet not dead. A prey to hope-sickness. All the languages but mine were spoken in the world. All the books except the one I wanted to read were writing to me. No one had ever written it. I thought only of the Being, my whole life spent longing for a glimpse of the Smile which would have acknowledged me—instead of the blank wall. The face that would have stopped my face from fading away. In bed with no arms, no letter, no pen. The right

105

moment: when one single word would have brought you back to life. Not even a word, a sound; the hint of a name; even if it wasn't spoken for you; even if it had been written in a book that had ended long ago. The day you went through all the books and only found the mere promise of that name, and even then perhaps you forced the text to concede even that faint possibility; the day when all the lives you had chased after in delusion because you thought you heard one of the notes of the beloved's name ringing in their call, leading you back to the same bed; that day, if the phone had rung once only instead of ringing so insistently, you could still have put off the last moment for one more lifetime—you'll be kept alive by doubt—that one ring might have been announcing a new sign.

The telephone kept on ringing. It was over. From now on the best weapon was not to have one at all. When you have a weapon you think you are going to defend yourself—that's just to let yourself be destroyed more easily. If you don't have a weapon you can stop yourself wanting to escape—not that you want to live, but the body is afraid to feel itself dying. Condemned? What joy! It was the last chance. The truth test at last. Being finally condemned freed me. When you are about to come to the end you may do everything you wouldn't have done before, for fear of precipitating that end; you can make the gesture you were suppressing to avoid attracting death's attention. It is like giving birth! You are lying on the bed, absorbed in what is taking place, as if you were the universe. Nature commands and you are nature. No one can prevent a little round head from emerging from between your thighs—what joy! Truth is coming out of your entrails, no one can contradict it. Nothing forbids you writing the letters, which you had to reject when you hadn't yet reached your time, for fear they would be unwelcome; in case they went too far. The letters it was better not to send, in case they arrived; caused harm; propelled events towards the truth; when you probably still thought that you had

106

something to protect; a body to wound; to spare; a hope you didn't want to have. A doubt you didn't want to arise. You played dead. Afraid that the man with the smile would answer with his silence. But when the last hour has come, let the head emerge, let the letter come out, a real little body—and you don't take it back again with both hands, between your legs, just as it is going to fly off. You may cut the cord yourself with no guilt. The letter goes off. If it's a complaint it's got nothing to do with you any more.

Being condemned is liberating; all the books said so. Despair is no longer a crime. You are free to send your final protest to the man you are missing. 'One word from you would have brought me back to life. What would I care about dying if only I could know what stopped you from pronouncing it.' Your first letters of Rebellion. I am shifting the weight on my heart.

They don't want me to live! They didn't want me to trust! They want me to be lost. No regrets. One last sorrow. Telegram immediately: '*Beloved*. It's over. I did so want to see you with my own eyes watching me die.'

Luckily he isn't there. Who knows who would be watching you?

I had dropped the book before the last chapter. No use reading what follows, it's over. There's a mistake. Because of the Parting. It's a question of *trompe l'oeil*. Because you have gone through the wilderness, through over-crowded schools, through tunnels, through deserts without being *looked at*, you end up at the foot of the last mountain, you kill yourself trying to climb it with the last strength of your soul. In books they wrote that at the end, once at the top, you would be able to see, but for dubious reasons, when you have reached the end of the world, all that your eyes see is a wall. And no one to look at me. All the Partings have come together to build the wall that invites you to lie down. Alone.

What would I care about dying if I could once let him know: 'Dearest friend, I cannot die without you dying too.' I

107

see my death ahead of me and I know you will be buried in the same coffin. More than three days inside myself, raking up these sorrowful thoughts while the telephone rings as loud as it can. *Beloved*, what loneliness, god wants me to die a mother. And as the torture continues I am thrilled by the threat: the phone ringing like mad—thunder and lightning—and the ceiling is so dark that you'd think you were at sea. And it's a brutal threat—like the calm which follows this storm.

Alas! my tomb will be a mother to me. I would have liked, above all else, to die in you. No one to tell you, but there will be a letter to announce: '*Nun hat die arme Seele Ruhe.*' Peace.

I was in the Bed of Bereavement, filled with sorrow, worn out with waiting. I had exhausted all the strength in my body desiring and being frustrated. I was at the head of the bed, lying against the wall, the black sheet over my head. Memory winding upstream, downstream, backwards and forwards, but the bed didn't move forwards. What's the use of skipping over the past, the telephone sounded the death knell. I would have already answered it, if only I could have spoken to the man with the smile: 'Dearest friend, This is it. Come quickly and say one word of farewell to me.' Perhaps I would have stayed in bed; perhaps he would have come; what does it matter; At least I would have left him this sign of suffering. But no messenger; the phone was engaged; no way of getting hold of him. Of dealing him the death blow. Love only gives in to death after dictating its last cruel Will.

Life wanted me to hide. I couldn't stay in bed till the last page. Dearest friend, I waited for you till the last chapter but one. Space is limited, the house lacks resources. No hole, no hovel. Everything is conspiring to hand me over to the first comer. I wanted to hide under the bed which was near, but I didn't want to please death. And what if Tantris comes, the unhoped for beloved, his dancer's body, his stern beautiful face—just when you were going out? Joy! Clasp him in your arms, embrace him. Misery! Death is on the stairs—the price of that consolation. He couldn't defend you. No arms. You half expected it. Not quite though. He should have come armed. Something alarming must have prevented him. Things were bound to turn out as if one of us had anticipated death. But he did not come. 'Farewell my loved one, my far-away one.' No one on the stairs. 'You won't have seen me die.' The stairs were endless.

As you go down you rake up hideous thoughts. More than three days of torture, rain, tears, shame, remorse, and the soul quite unbalanced. In the end my cries died down.

And I went out, taking care not to turn my head.

Death must have gone in. I guessed it was there by the silence.

You went out? After such violence, you are so tense that there is still a little death in your heart, a taste of blood in your mouth that you can't get rid of. From now on you can never forget why you are mortal.

Go on, go on.

Outside, but in the darkness. That night nothing could stop you, no memories, no anguish, no cops. Not the biblical winds which make the dead turn back, not the steely rain. My tenacity was rewarded. A taxi stopped. Life itself had ordered it. I got in. Never mind if it wasn't life—the fact that I had been stronger than death that day made all gestures irresistibly reassuring. I was sitting in the back, not knowing where I was being taken, through which city, to what trial of loneliness—it was the night of the first Mourning. I didn't know who was going to be buried, who would pay with his blood. Soon I would have to know; I would know forever what body I was coming to.

The news had spread, the wind scoured the open sea, beds were grounded. In the street you could have seen a crowd rushing towards the body, if your eyes had not been filled with black tears which blurred your vision.

And there you are in the procession going to get the body: the army, police, all the forces of Anguish are not without their suspicions that you are the murderer. And you are not far from believing it either. But as long as there is no proof, no motive . . . The importance of the murder could be gauged by the grave atmosphere and the stir it caused. Wipe your eyes. Wait before you fling yourself into deep mourning until you know who has deserted you, who didn't wait for you. Hear the moans, cries, beating of breasts. Suddenly, take in, in one glance, the funeral procession.

How could you fail to be impressed by the enormous grey marble sarcophagos placed at the head of the procession? It could hold ten giants. How could you fail to be impressed by the pomp? By the idea of a sarcophagus, in this day and age? All the details were meaningful to me: 'It's you; your murder, the body you forgot; your most ancient past; your most recent past; that is coming back; a tomb containing all the beds.' What does the name of the corpse matter, whether it's real, whose face it would remind you of? The corpse is the proof. Perhaps it will be none other than the death that lived inside you when you were rotting with life.

And there you are at the centre of the scene, in the room where it had been set down; perhaps it is none other than the body that was dearest to you. There you are again beside the body which is going to be lifted up. It's huge corpse laid under a black silk flag.

You knew him by his size. None other than he who grows big in death; from death to death. And while he was being carried away I felt he was growing still bigger—the sarcophagos would not hold him, he would not be able to be buried.

I stayed in the room alone. Ten years later the air smelled of his blood. In the deathbed there were bundles of paper, notebooks, all the books you would have to write to enable you to bury his name under a pyramid of words; envelopes addressed to me for the letters he had not sent; and several notebooks of failures. Pick them up quickly, tear them up carefully before you have time to see your name printed on them.

This corpse calls for an explanation. Why not give it to you? Didn't you part from it chapters ago? Years ago? What are you waiting for to kill it off? Your death no longer depends on his signature. What is stopping you from burying it? From writing the story that would manage to do it, to end your trial?

I'm afraid to hear myself speak.—What have you done?—I have known death.—Be frank.—Death has known me—Be frank—I have made love with death. How I wish there was nothing left! When will I be acquitted? Will I never be at peace?

It is no use carrying away the corpse, imprisoning it in its sarcophagos—the empty room is filled with death.

*   *   *

Here is the original fear. I didn't make up this story. I swear I want to tell the truth. Those who have lived it have gone silent: that's why it is so difficult to get at. You would have to cut the throat of silence itself to tear out the story. I emerged from the well of truth. Half stifled. Five thousand years could go by and I still wouldn't be able to ease the pain. Half mad. The other half lost. Ten years and the wound still gapes. The blood won't clot. The wound in his lungs. The hole in the breast. The wound in my breast. The hand at my throat that won't let go. It's not that I haven't wanted to tell the story before. Besides, I have always known that everything truthful I might say about it would ring false. I have seen the glaring truth.

One page would do. Ten years. And five thousand pages have been torn up. As soon as I tried to write the truth the page slipped away, the paper refused to take the ink, the page turned

111

over, my pen ran out, space was stained with black blood-clots, they were all over my fingers, everything ran with blood, even my eyes, and the words were wounded—terrifying—as if the truth was afraid of being written down.

And I was afraid for the sake of truth, as I had feared for the safety of the loved one's body, because it was so extremely fragile; as the being I loved feared too much light after The Fatal Illness.

If you say: 'I have seen myself dying. I have seen my soul on fire in my body, I have seen my heart burst into flames in my breast, I have seen my life dying in my flesh,' who would understand you?

That is why you have to approach the truth with the utmost caution. Because it is deadly. One letter too many and all would be lost forever.

In the other language his name began with the letter S. That was his other name, but I didn't know; the name for his other self. Another of his names began with the letter V or F, depending on which language you were using. I never knew his real name. I didn't even know he had one. To get the names sorted out I would have had to know what to think of this: the Meeting. It took place 'in another country'.

At that time I was particularly susceptible to what happened inside in languages or between languages. I had too good an ear. Things were forever meaning something else. For example: when I saw him for the first time in the middle of a deceptive May I was sure it meant 'You may be deceived.' That alarmed me, I resisted, I did all I could not to doubt. There was no dividing line between bodies and words; I couldn't tell how sense was made. But I felt that languages were being translated one into another and I couldn't stop them. I was living over the reading-rooms at the top of a famous tower whose name I have forgotten; it was reserved for re-search. It was an unpleasant building with no windows. I didn't like the materials it was made of: marble, granite, bronze and lead. The place was so far from the sea that I wondered if I would ever see it again, in my Lifetime. I was into books of Bereavement, worn out by reading.

As I write this very line the memory of the books that were tormenting me comes back. Their titles began with D, death's initial, the name God bears when he reveals himself. One of these texts was by Donne—I don't want to go back to it. The English Donne turned French on me; challenged me: Give. Names were ordering me about. In the state I was in, just after my serious illness, how could I have disobeyed? 'Give.' I gave. 'Give.' I did.

You can talk about the day, the night, the light, the attraction, the beginning, the pain of searching for life, hoping, desiring; the suspense, the pain of losing yourself before love. You can speak of your ugliness, your split self; you can talk about your illnesses, your obscene thoughts, your shame, your crime; you have the strength to reveal what you should not admit. You may reveal what should stay hidden. But it is almost impossible for you to speak of your dread of god, the one you worshipped. There has already been so much bloodshed, the pain doesn't fade, it is as intense as ever—worthy of its divine origin. You can bear to speak of the truth and watch the blood running out of your mouth; you can watch your hands burning, the fingers that have caressed the skin of a god turn black and shrivel up and you didn't sink through the floor—your soul is covered in crap—even with a grub for the tongue in your mouth it is easier to tell how, with that tongue, you denied your mother and your father, how you cast out your mother and your father from your memory, from your body; you killed them in your flesh and they rotted in your thoughts, you were stinking, you didn't regret it since god had asked you to do it . . . It is easier to tell all this than to reveal the secret of the one you worshipped.

How hard it is to talk about the Trial, the one I could never bring myself to speak about without puking up tongue and lungs. For five thousand years on the edge of the abyss, The Great Humiliation stuck in my throat. The thing I couldn't swallow or bring up. Stuck in your memory, and I have never managed to stomach it or to write about it.

To begin this account, to make the first move, took ten years.

Someone came into my room before sunrise with the inexorable determination of the day. I was lying in sleep as the soul in sickness: held there without giving in to it completely. My thoughts were 'awake.' *Behold I shew you a mystery, we shall not all sleep*, this man had The—smile.

Something heavier than death was crushing me. I had seen that smile before upsetting my mother's face. If the stranger had been bigger I would have kept my distance. But he was of human height. I had had a sleepless night. That smile must have been mirrored on my face when I heard that my first son was dead: a real death. It had had its place, its hour. 'In another country,' one day when I wasn't there. I had a son whom they said was dead; but his dying wasn't over. As if he had never been born. Nothing had separated us; except a hospital window, a sea, distance, the tricks played by absence. A sentence of my mother. And the twitching of her lips around the word death.

There was nothing to tell about that death. Except this: it wouldn't go away. It was still in my air. Anyway, I had put it off till later. These things happen. Deaths that are too frail, whose corpses are too light or too disturbing for us. I had noted that several times before. Perhaps these abortive deaths prepared the way to the last room. As if the absence of my dead had freed the bed for the last scene.

How can I say how unexpected it was? How unexpected *I* was?

—Isn't it time to part with the secret by writing it down; time to live and so get beyond it; time to tear yourself out of love's breast by opening your mouth and breaking the

114

silence; time to get out of the room by protesting?—But in order to write it down I would have to be out already.

You have tried a hundred times in vain. To get out you would have to part with god the incomprehensible by understanding him; having understood him, leave the room in one go, by writing it down in one go; bar the door, break it down at last, draw the line, have done with the infinite for once; at least once and you'd have to tell yourself every time: I haven't quite made it yet.

A longing stronger than my will kept me in the room. Held for ten years by another in that purity, stifling within its walls. You are like the mad prophet railing against the madness of his god. Angry even unto death. Like writing raging against the silence, *I am wonderfully and fearfully made*, that both creates it and holds it back. *And such knowledge too excellent for me*—And understands it only too well. Angry even unto death. You wanted to get out of the city by protesting: you'd rather die than be kept pure inside; you wanted to slam the door on it rather than be imprisoned in the purity that protects you from everything; held by someone else—you have wanted to get out for a thousand years and have never done it.

Perhaps your longing, fearing, intending to get out means that, although you haven't managed it yet, you are getting there.

Those who know they are dying know that '*not* wanting' contains a great deal of 'wanting': it's only a question of a door; a fear; a page; and perhaps it would only need a word, but a word that isn't misleading, that comes straight from your heart's desire and won't be twisted.

What if you said the word? Every time I have wanted to tell the truth I have lied. It couldn't come out. I chose to use analogies which I vaguely felt would save the truth. It wouldn't be harmed by being written down. What if you did manage it? I don't think I shall. What's the use of opening your eyes if the window is curtained? What's the good of tearing off your eyelids if the room is in darkness? As if the

115

truth were anxious not to be told, by me. Out of respect. If I did succeed it would mean I had failed. I would have brought it down to my level. That is what you are afraid of wanting to do. We are bound together by a hatred beyond words.

Do you want to shape the infinite? Drag down to earth what has never bowed down? Bury the eternal? Get god on paper? Send him off in an envelope? To whom? To the self that no longer exists.

If the duel your writing is fighting against death, that brings it so close to death that it is drawn to it by tenderness and hostility; if the battle that binds them together were to end in your victory, in death's defeat—you would never lift your pen. *Death's duel.* Luckily it is *death's* duel. The outcome is still uncertain. In so far as you are mortal you have always written on the understanding that you would not lose death; the supreme death; you write to make sure of it; so that you feel your mortality; to feel that death understands you; that you haven't lost the secret.

You write in terror. Because of nostalgia: you are forced to admit to yourself that you cling to the room of your suffering as you would cling to the greatest joy. You write in hope and dread. You cannot brush aside the thought that dares to bring you back to the worst: 'I shouldn't have left.' You don't really know the things you knew in the room, you didn't understand them. You haven't held on to them. If they didn't have just a little hold over you, that would be that. You didn't get out, there was no way out. The truth is that you couldn't stay. You were suddenly thrown out. The god of madness let you down.

You are writing against the law of no-return. You don't know how to return. You think that it can only be done by a superhuman effort—and perhaps that isn't possible any more. You are afraid of finding the words that would manage to get back to the room. You despair of finding them. How could words destroy the secret when the secret of the room was precisely to lure the words away from your language, drive them crazy, stifle the most reckless ones? He spoke to you in the other language. When you spoke that other language you understood eternity. You can't translate the eternal into your own language; you don't feel you have the right to speak the language of eternity any more. Because of this past stay you can't stop longing to hear it bewitching you again; separating you from everyone.

Sometimes the pain dies down; then there is a feeling of infinite sweetness, as if all the suffering had turned into the love it had tormented, coming back in tears of fire.

Almost all my pain has vanished, but that doesn't matter. All is lost but death. The Thought: 'You have been through what you will never be able to live through ever again,' excites me, I am pierced with a keen joy in which there is the pain of unique suffering. You only learn how to die once. You can only be destroyed the first time. The second time you defend yourself. It will never ever happen again. I have lost the first death. Its slow progress ending in nothingness. Once you have known Great Suffering you don't get over it. It might never have happened. You fled from it like the plague, like shame; you cursed and hated it, and now you tremble with terror at the idea that death could forsake you. Could have condemned you to live. Without it. Condemned you to see the light without the darkness. Perhaps death has withdrawn from you forever what it had given with the violence that you worship, trembling. The unique violence be means of which death gave up its life to you.

Hold on to it in sorrow, fight to keep it, in fear and regret, with phrases that wound it, degrade it, threaten it with death: 'It might never have happened.' 'Death came to me. The one that never comes. But because it did come once it couldn't happen again to the woman I am now.' I am still here to grieve over it.

Haven't you been through other deaths? I fell three times

into the bed death had liberated. But it was all over, already. I didn't die. Death didn't come. Life let me down. A window opened.

The body I hurled out had nothing left to lose. My other deaths didn't follow my first death as phoenix follows phoenix, but as childhood comes after birth—killing it off.

It was my first experience of death. Death came to me in person and I didn't know its name. The shadows in the room made all light seem dark. Death taught me to die.

Contrary to everything I may have thought, told myself, wished to write, what happened in the room had not stopped happening. Something is still going on. A pain I am nursing. A fear I am fostering, that reminds me: 'don't forget you are mortal.' I cling to it as proof that I have lived; that I have learnt; that I will know. The agony has gone away. If the pain faded completely I would be dead, or I would die. I do almost everything I can to keep hold of it. How hard it is to hang on to death! I have long been afraid that writing would kill it, in the end.

The battle continues. I was afraid of winning. Of losing.

A desert lies between your Loss and the names you call it. The desert that allows you regret, indulgence in your sorrow, and your fighting spirit. You can take notes, cover the earth's surface with words, move towards suffering with the help of an infinite number of struggling letters, with no fear for the death of the desert; for your death; you can see your recent suffering spring to meet you and you are afraid, an accomplice; the face cannot change, it's the face behind all faces; and after running away for ten years, when you turn round, even after five thousand years, you can see that death in person is there—your dream come true. Death hasn't lost sight of you, it has followed you, only waiting for a sign from you to join you again. Then you shout out its names very loudly, all the loving names that it didn't fail to respond to; but you don't have to run away since you know that even if your ruin in person managed to get through the desert, *Come*!

Come! even if you gave it your hand, I am coming, it wouldn't
have a chance to carry you away, to lead you back to the bed.
The room is shut up. When you left, distraught, ten years ago,
the keys stayed on the inside, the door slammed. Such a rigid
door once closed, as if you could never open it again. You
can't bring yourself to lose sight of it.

The room has not vanished. No one is forbidding you to
enter it again. You knew a terrifying delight in that room; the
infernal joy that paradise reserves for those mortals who dare
to reach it; the place where you are given something when
you have given up asking for anything. Suddenly you have
everything: to lose. The joy that attracts death and drives it
mad with jealousy. You have loved love in person, you have
known unswerving desire; trembling, you have loved un-
compromisingly; you have followed love further than is
possible, gone beyond yourself, beyond all knowledge, ahead
of life itself, without flinching, right up to the room whose
entrance death alone guards. You have seen love take the test
of immortality; dictate its last Will to death. No one is
forbidding you to try again. But you are afraid of discovering
that you no longer have the strength to wrestle with Loss.
Because death can only be mastered by that strangely
frivolous being who has no mercy on himself.

I had followed love coming right up against death until I
reached absolute solitude.

I wasn't expecting anyone.

It was him. His way of not coming in: of being in my room
as if I were in His. Walking in unannounced. Although I
certainly didn't know everything, I was already struck. From
then on I was concerned with the way he struck me—like a
gentle thunderbolt; his way of bringing my soul to life; to
death, with the same accurate stroke, beyond knowledge,
beyond truth and falsehood, beyond good and the evil of loss.

I was already carried away. His way of breaking over me.
Unawares, I was already surrounded on all sides, he had

119

penetrated my deepest secrets. As if I had committed an indiscretion and so handed him all the keys to myself. The violence of his non-violence: a veiled violence. He didn't come in: it was I who was suddenly face to face with him. Instead of asking him to go out I felt embarrassed. I was lying down in front of him, my thoughts in confusion, my body covered in bad memories. I felt unclean. Because of the smile he flung out at me. It was a determined smile: obviously nothing could alter it. I was hiding in my sheets, in my chaos, in my dung; crumpled, on edge, contorted; taken by surprise in the midst of my iniquities; spewed out, up to my neck in nightmares and disasters.

I had not been expecting anyone. I found myself in front of him. The Unexpected in person. He was standing before my bed, as if I had willed his presence. The stranger, instantly recognized as the-one-you-were-not-expecting. With the unquestionable self-possession of the unthinkable.

It is only today that the thought occurs to me: 'at this precise moment the whole story of my death has been decided.' What was happening in the room did not leave me the time nor the inclination to think. Things were going so fast that I was always falling behind. Directions were taken, paths pointed out, my movements suggested; a dialogue was going on, an oracle was overturned; the questions he asked me answered the questions I would only ever have dared ask myself; or god if he had existed. They were dangerous. Had he seen through me?

Things escaped from me and were taken up by the other. What I had never had was coming back to me. I had to admit that I had, doubtless, always known what I had just learnt—I had to acknowledge it. I believed he was reading my thoughts. There was a will in that room way ahead of me. As if my business was his; as if he had not only taken charge of my desires but of my destiny.

Perhaps he wasn't reading my thoughts. I thought he was.

No time to check. I was falling behind at every sentence. I listened. Suspicious. Startled. I couldn't grasp the meaning; couldn't catch up. I was totally bewildered. I didn't understand anything. Though I didn't realize it at the time. Trying to grasp ten things at once, like chasing ten hares at a time. Even if I'd been ten dogs I would have been outrun; because the hares were continually turning into something else. A hunter was amusing himself.

He talked to me without hesitation in his own language. As if he were sure that I would understand it; that I had to hear it. It wasn't mine. It was a strange language whose pronouns came straight for me at every turn, pitilessly. A positive language. I couldn't say no. And he left no place in his voice for doubt. It was a voice that checked me, frightened me; made me want to run away, kept me willingly riveted to the bed which I couldn't leave, where I had gone to ground; buried myself; shrunk, felt myself getting younger and forgetting.

His tone was weary, yet deep and disturbingly calm. The voice of a survivor. God knows what languages it had gone through, what silences it had conquered amidst prayers and sobs, what corpses it had had to wrench itself free from in order to reach that low, serious pitch. That soothing tone that was crushing me. I was lying under his words, Jonah in the bottom of the boat. Escaping in my pretend-sleep: eternity broke loose; I was in my night-gown, ashamed, sick. He was addressing doubt personnified: me: 'I woke you up.' It was not a question; he was announcing what had occurred. 'I woke you up.' 'Yes.' His peaceful voice, torn from so many battles, weighed on my chest heavier than death. To wake up done in, in the ship's hold. The boat thought it would be dashed to pieces. Instead of going to Nineveh, you had tried to escape to Tarshish.

'Get up.' I was awake. I suspected it was the last awakening. The first or the last. The one that put paid to my longing for sleep. The one that pulls you out of the hold

121

forever, pulls you from your soul's abysmal depths. To cast you forth into the sea. And you stay in its fish belly. You will sleep no more. Sleep won't come again. At that time I stopped sleeping. In the calm of his voice was the tremor of storms that had died down. I weathered the echo of torments that I couldn't imagine. His voice came from another time. All the waves and all the tears of several lifetimes washed over me. He wasn't yet thirty.

Is it by chance that in order to talk about the Trial I have finally been forced to return to the first bed? When I wanted to go back into the back room the door opened onto the first room. As if I couldn't get to the final scene. I have to go back through the three rooms, because truth wants me to. Perhaps it was because of what happened in the room where he was not expected. At times, because of my anguish, I think that the three rooms where we were struggling for our lives were only the same room lived in differently. This isn't completely untrue. If there had been ten rooms, ten lives to threaten, to save, ten deaths to die, I think things would have been arranged by the same secret authority for similar scenarios to be played out. There must have been one basic scene; unknown to me; but I can't have realized it, everything was arranged between the door and the bed. A battle was going on. I didn't notice the similarity until after the last replay. Sometimes I wonder whether the outcome hadn't been decided by our respective positions when the door opened: wasn't I still lying in bed? having already gone down among my dead? I didn't dare get up. 'Come! Let's go to Nineveh for a coffee.' His eyes on me, without the slightest embarassment. My head almost burst. He was the one who *looks*. I asked him to turn round while I dressed quickly. I hid myself, clothed myself, didn't show myself to anyone, not to him, not to myself, mirrors made me look away.

*

It is very possible that the crucial scene had been set up for me in a previous story, outside me, outside the room. And so what I took for the beginning was nothing but the final revelation. All those who have watched themselves dying come to that conclusion. Ten years later you make the dubious discovery that when you were *not* waiting for anyone, you were, deep down, expecting someone; Else. The door opens. The person who comes in is so calm that your story halts. It can only be life or death. It can only be life—nothing—but—life.

When you were slipping on your dress he told you his name. He had his back to you. His three names hurt your ears. They were your son's names. Chance was on his side. Or a will more impressive than chance. Hadn't you heard the echo of another voice in his, reproaching you? What are you doing here, sleepy-head? Get up! Can't you hear the voice of voices? What is attracting death's frightening attention to you? Can't you hear death announcing itself? Reminding you of its three names? No room to think about it. You were already taken over—in case you thought of running away.

Nothing that happened between the first and the last room can be wiped out. Somewhere everything goes on, the torment continues in the past eternal. Every moment was lost, mourned, saved, as it was happening. I wasn't living, each gesture was a repetition, from way back in the past, after the separation, life was returning to life, nostalgic; I was looking at myself from the point of view of the eternal, once all was lost, and I wept in anguish.

In the city of Nineveh you went through what you can never live over again; every move over forever—the stranger was guiding me. I hadn't expected anyone. The night before I only had one desire: to lie under a ricinus and ask for the end. I was tired of life, far from the world. 'I've had enough, oh time, let me go to sleep.' Now, despite myself, I was up and dressed—(get up and eat.) I was in the streets and the Present was by my side.

123

I didn't like the Present: his way of being calmly by himself, beside me, as if no one could disturb him, disturbed me. My nearness didn't change him at all. He could have been alone. He was stopping me from being alone and at the same time recalling me to my greater inner loneliness. And besides, something about his appearance stopped me from really seeing him, as if he were too much himself. Uniquely himself. And as if there was no one in Nineveh, no one round us at the bar, and no one beside him. And yet he turned to me, addressed me, as if he had been open to me from the very start. He allowed himself to be looked at without drawing back, without hiding a thought, he presented all his faces, not withholding a single one, unblinking, as if he wasn't being looked at, but bathed in a mysterious light. He irritated me. I was hardly out of my dazed, mindless state. His self-assurance paralysed me. His way of being there, as if he had been rushed to Nineveh because of me. He hadn't sought it. Nature had decided it. He was obeying strange laws. As if he were willingly submitting to the will of a god. With a strength in submission equal to that will. While we were having coffee. His name at that time was Mensch. He assured me that was his real name. He was smiling, looking steadily at me, smiling.

Perhaps you had understood that morning who S. was. But it wasn't the right moment. That would come later. In the bar you were still in the position of the prophet dazed with fear, so worn out by his vigils, that he doesn't distinguish between 'knowing' and 'knowing that he knows.' He doesn't dare understand what he has understood. His smile was stopping you from looking at him. From thinking. His huge, brutal presence: nothing could have checked that presence, put it off, as if he were the Voice. He was weighing me down: a sly, even pressure which made me bristle. The weight of a colossal calm penetrating me. The force of a colossal silence weighing me down. I didn't dare block my ears.

I was sure he was doing it on purpose. That was a crazy

thought. His way of being near without coming nearer, his keeping me away, repulsed me. I was flung out at a hopeless distance from him: when I touched bottom, in my innermost self, I still did not escape him, whereas he never ceased to be unapproachable. Daunting. He brushed against me on all sides, I was caught, imprisoned, restricted, but I never got to him. Continually drawing back, I was forestalled, anticipated and had the alarming feeling that I could not escape from his territory.

In the bar at Nineveh his familiarity shocked me. The glass pane that divided him from me did not protect me from him. He could stretch out his hand and put it on my arm. I should have pushed it away. But it was a strange, kind hand, which was trying to convey to my skin the secret of its light touch. It was trembling: 'My strength is in my weakness.'

He talked to me as if he were talking to himself, unpretentiously, as if no one was listening to him, in a low disturbing voice. As if all I was was a moment of himself. I felt I was hearing what should never have been heard. In the street his voice was too serious. He was laughing. His trembling arm slipped round my waist. How did I allow it? I didn't push it away. Because I was weak; a calm weakness that alarmed me. His fragility weighed on me unbearably. This being was too light. He made me think of death and I took the blame on myself, to avoid blaming him. He seemed about to fall over any moment. I was humiliated. I felt cheated. I was to blame.

I wanted to run away at every step; to wake up; I wanted it to be just a dream. His words forbade me. The clairvoyant, mysterious phrases, their shadowy texture, their fabric of threats. A day-spider, a night-spider, which was going to gobble me up?

His transparent sentences staggered me. You would have thought he was speaking for me. That was my fear. His fear. 'Wasn't the story fraught enough? Confused enough?' His leap over anguish, my very anguish. 'You can prevent what I

125

was expecting from happening. Your Youth.' As if my youth wasn't young, but ancient and definitive, because it was formed in an ageless time. 'That proves your strength. It doesn't prove how strong my trust is. It proves my immense weakness.' Things I might have said to him. That your strength frightens me. If I hadn't been cut off from myself. By each one of his phrases. 'I had just fallen asleep. And here you are coming to frighten me.' His regrets. My mute reproaches. How to describe the gaiety in his dread? When all was settled. The weariness in his flights of enthusiasm? And now I mustn't sleep any more. The flaunting of his weakness, as if he wanted to dazzle me. His way of glorifying it. With a gloomy admiration. How to understand his audacious diffidence? His morbid sentences too charged with sadness to be anything but oppressive. Like children they were calling me to come and help them. Their heads under the black sheets. As if they were afraid of not being heard. By me. Afraid of dying. Choked with suppressed tears. I was filled with mistrust. They fed on a mystery. Perhaps a poison. A hint of fear. Pleasure in terror. Perhaps nothing but a lie. The effect of a prophetic dream. I was filled with dread. Perhaps there was a danger. Why not name it? As if he were afraid of reprisals. If it was a question of dying, why not bring it out into the open? I wouldn't have listened to him anyway. It was a question of having lost the way. They boasted of being lost. I was lost too. 'Yesterday I was so alone.' The glass pane. 'I couldn't even love any more. Every impulse came up against a pane of glass. I couldn't touch anything any more. I was without a single living contact. Yesterday I . . . Everything came back to me, obliterated.

And now here I am wanting to touch you. When I can hardly get up. When you have come too late. When I had just made my peace. It proves you can never be sure of anything. What a state I'm in. And I can't lie down any more. My peace was so short-lived! I was so alone, so calm, fully prepared not to get up again.'

But the anguish was different. The contorted black phrases were strained to breaking point, shattering and wounding me.

'I would have liked to be able to live.' But I didn't want to. 'I was like someone dying of thirst who hasn't the strength left to drink. That's how thirsty I was for love.' Perhaps I wanted 'to want', I would have been afraid of being punished. I abhorred what I longed for. I could only long for the worst. And any way, I didn't want to.

The whole difference was there: *he* spoke of himself with pity. As if he were talking of a god-like friend who had taken his last farewell. He was distancing himself to avoid seeing himself disappear. And now I was calling him back to the cruel bed. And *I* felt a pitiless hatred for myself. It wasn't the same glass pane.

The black words were avoiding something that must have been foul. He didn't 'say' them. He 'put them forward'. They didn't wind their way towards me. They hedged. 'You came at the right time for another!' Their power, craftiness—I was stung. Taken in. Their spidery legs. Their web of metaphors, smothered innuendos. I was summoned, pressed, beseeched. Accused of being slow, cautious. Recruited for a war. Without knowing the enemy. I didn't come looking for you. No one was holding me back. He was expecting me to join him in a quarrel whose origin I didn't know. A battle was beginning all over again. It was my fault. When I meet you on the day before the last. Complaints had been lodged. I was struggling in the web.

I suspected him of wanting to fabricate a story for himself. To trap me in. I felt I was turning into his fly. His food. A story to slow things down, so that he could enjoy it without reservation. But he himself was buzzing, writhing in the web.

He was playing chess with himself. He didn't place a word until he had measured his chances of protecting it. On the defensive. All the sentences calculated with an enemy in mind. Frenzied negotiations taking place, round the inevitable. Keep your distance. Keep quiet. Send out thoughts to reconnoitre. To test out the battle field. Instead of doves. Moles. Night butterflies. Seductive messages. They came back saying: 'fear, helplessness, hesitation.' With an incredible force that roused my disbelief. But the body didn't lie. 'I long to be able to love.' His light-hearted laughter. 'I really must have managed to shift . . . Good for me!' Joy despite the heavy note in his voice. He had shifted silence. But it didn't last. He was serious again. Flight, cowardice, deadly weariness. Given what was to come: 'Whereas every day this month I have been pushed to the brink.'

It was a question of a journey: 'What if I came back?' A temptation: 'It is not getting there that I am afraid of now.' And the anguish that wasn't mine, that was trying to gain my favour, my patience; to cling on to my unconscious. With the obstinacy of a child clinging to the skirts of life. This blackmail disgusted me. 'I am afraid you'll get me wrong. My weakness is not blackmail. My fear is not weakness.' Found out! Entangled more and more deeply in a mysterious connection to the Present. Since he was asking me: 'Don't hate me, please,' at the very moment I was beginning to hate him without knowing why. And so, driven from my cover, forestalled, more and more uncertain, and not daring to detest him: like the unbeliever obsessed with god who is wondering whether he will have to confess himself a believer, just to get god out of the way. But he was saying to me: 'Today I have nothing to say in my favour. Once I come back, I will show you the best.'

His lamentations moved me, put me off. Do those in league with death have a language to sing death's praises in? My hostility welled up, overflowed. Who told you the name of the enemy? Perhaps it's someone else sheltering inside him? Who has come back to die? A battle was going on inside his body. His arm round my waist, too intimate, an error crept in, his voice was too naked, a feeling of obscenity. 'I dreamt that I was living. I was surprised. I said to myself I only hope it isn't a dream.'

His dreams of death. He was laughing. I had trouble laughing. The way his deaths lived inside him. This fairy-tale, or else it was a secret belief held by his people: they say that if someone who is dying manages to attract to him a human being who has never heard of death, and who has never pronounced death's name, he would be saved. His voice had the power to re-call the dead. Mine came back too. To Nineveh. To help him. The obscure, the insignificant, the lost, despite my protest. They hurled themselves upon me through him. They were in collusion: there was a link between their bodies and his—a particular kind of suffering. Something that went straight to my heart. They climbed over his chest. They were aiming for mine. My point of absolute vulnerability. This was the mystery: in the lungs, between the breasts; I felt it ploughing up my breast, thumping: another heart come to attack mine. I knew them by their cough. Their voices hoarse with blood. Their lungs pierced with bullets. Their mouldy, blackened bronchi, their chests caved in. Their death-rattle, like the howling of wolves. Their filthy bleeding. Their deadly silence. Their secret spittle. The way they slipped off like thieves. Their loneliness.

And so it was them! The ones I hadn't seen disappearing, the shameful dead. The illicitly buried. Another blow from one of my fathers! Their craving for vengeance. Their jealousy. (They should have made the effort before.) Their craving to be mourned. To make me pay for their defeat. To put their sickness, their mortality on me. To make the most of my body until I go mad. Until they die.

An ominous joke: your father's letter in 1935: 'My love, I don't think I am deluding myself when I say to you that I foresee a brilliant future.' Return it to the 'presumed dead'. With your sincere illusions. Never be sure of the morrow.

What are you doing here, sleepy-head! Quick, get up, can't

you feel your life's on fire? Perhaps you knew who M was this morning, but you let yourself forget. And now, how can you wake up?

According to one of his stories he was once a young man from Mord. At that time he was called Man. Or perhaps that's his real name now? He has changed his name several times and begun life again in different countries. In my opinion he was a wandering Jew. He didn't deny it. He had devoted himself to writing. If you had been at their marriage you would probably have caught a glimpse of the truth, just an outline: seeing the couple sitting at the table of the law, and despite the light bridal veil you would have seen that M. was a young woman with a prodigiously strong intellect and she was marrying a woman then called Schreiber. That didn't fail to cause a stir in the world since there had never been such a marriage before. But M. had always had an iron will. A steady clear gaze. The thought of his strangeness was always with you, you began to get used to it. Even if he were no one, at least he was a living proof of Presence. Proof of a radiant reality. I was stunned by his strangeness. What the hell were you doing there?

Instead of dragging round Nineveh, run off to Tarshish, get back to your senses; go back to the books that have been written, printed, arranged on shelves—their covers are dull, their pages filled with honeyed words and all their lies are true. But I didn't know where I was any more.

You have been trying since this morning to get back to your right mind and you don't know yourself. And yet you did leave your reason somewhere close by. The only thing you are sure of is that you took leave of your senses this morning just before you got up, that's logical. No use searching your memory, no trace of an image. But your reason is around. And you remember the last thought, just a word, more like a movement: Run away! You don't know Nineveh and besides, it is confusing, unsettling; even if you have the feeling you have tramped through all its streets, you must have got them

130

mixed up, or they've changed in your absence. Haven't you yourself changed? Didn't you end up that evening doing what you never should have done?

Didn't you find Your-self in the room alone with S, despite yourself. It was my room, but darker, the interior decor had been upset during the day, by chance. I was crouching on the divan, in the corner with no shield, with no reason, my wings folded; there was a whole network of threads in the air. I saw him cheerfully moving to and fro weaving, making knots, his proposals getting madder and madder, nearer and nearer. It was a question of my whole life. He was pulling it to pieces, I wasn't living it. He separated, unwound, killed, cut, picked through, eliminated, re-made me other distant and solitary lives. As if he were making love to my life, in his way, his head and neck moving, crossing-out, rewriting, pages, extracts. And all in praise of his fictions he was annihilating my reality. After all that, how could you hope to come to your senses in Nineveh? Your reason certainly is in Nineveh, but it's beyond you.

A chatterbox, I thought. Not just that. It was something else. I was trying to think what it was. Liar? Yes, a liar. Not really. It was a question of space: the distance separating me from the sense buried in his sentences seemed interminable. Or else I had little patience. I admit that the words weren't leaving me behind, they were beckoning, encouraging me. But from comma to full-stop I was getting more and more impatient; night fell in the end and I had hardly grasped a thing. It's his fault, I thought. That was not unfair: something couldn't be said. Could only be said in these 'flights.' HE was breaking through. But he needed someone to follow in his footsteps, to pick up the scent. 'I am not a chatterbox, believe me. I would be lying if I told you I know where I am leading you; but that's not what I want. As far as I know I am not trying to lead you astray. It's a matter of truth: it won't leave me in peace. It won't let me live, nor can I die unless I have done all I can to pursue it. I am not strong enough. I can't seek and find at the same time. But perhaps if you come with me I may be allowed to discover the truth.'

His confidence: 'You will know me as you have never known anyone else.' I understood less and less. His surprise: feigned, genuine: 'Your strength, courage, beauty, your path, purity, youth, vigour, innocence.' He saw in me everything he claimed he didn't have; I didn't recognize myself. His suffering: 'How can you not protest when the enemy declares: You will never live together. And yet I don't cry out.'

My weariness like the stars in the sky.

His spectacular chattering: like a giant, like a seer. Mad, 'how can I not go mad?' My disquiet like the shifting sands. He guessed too much. His way of embodying a whole people, saved, lost, led. His way of coming from all foreign lands across an even stranger land. His forty thousand wildernesses. Led by one person alone. Driven from every country. Reunited. His wealth of knowledge: he knew more than a thousand learned men.

His command of walls: he built them. Each sentence constructed like a wall to surround his people; called to me. I listened. I came: there was a wall, that he had just made. I could hear him panting on the other side of the thought that he'd had difficulty getting over; which I had neither the strength nor the desire to get over; but which rose up in front of me and communicated something of his excessive nature.

His secret: 'I would have to tell you about the thing locked away inside my breast, like in one of those wardrobes that it is forbidden for a woman to open.' I don't think I was at all curious.

He got up. Went towards my wardrobe. Perhaps he didn't, I would have hated him to tamper with it. Perhaps he was merely drawn to the space between the wardrobe and the door. I was coiled in the corner of the bed. He took off his shirt. I was going to scream. Why bother? His scent spread. I was going to close my eyes, get up, all my will to live was alerted—my wings freed, my power to flee.

And then that extraordinary incident took place which should have changed everything. It began by inflammation of the ceiling; all the walls in the room were inflamed, my ears, brain, throat. Then he coughed. In the city a strong, violent wind opened up the walls, broke down doors. Like the Voice of truth, literally. And the voice of life was not in that cough.

Fear was strongest. It was an angry, beseeching voice: he was suddenly in the centre of that storm. I was paralysed. I blocked my ears. Don't misunderstand me. I wasn't protecting myself. I wanted to spare him. I didn't want to have heard his voice.

That was nonsense: I hadn't stopped hearing it since the morning. The wardrobe had already been broken into before he coughed. My gesture meant: 'Let me not know anything about it.' Too late. The teacher was there. The mystery was solved: Dear Friend, you haven't much longer to live.

You didn't know how much you hated Sickness.

It took place in the breast. The story. The struggle.

You saw him go out in sorrow, into the storm. His sorrow, my relief. I went to the airport immediately. Found the plane ready to leave, as if it was just waiting for me. Running away from the presence of the Eternal. You paid the fare, got on board, went to work in Tarshish, far away from the presence of the Eternal. How short-sighted can you be!

His letters were waiting for me in Tarshish. Who gave him your address? He was different from other mortals. Had they arrived? Who knows what 'arrived' means? He didn't 'arrive'. He had made himself known to you in his cough, like god in the burning bush. Now, I didn't believe in god.

Today you are: a breast no longer speaking in flashes of

133

lightning and blood, but in words. And every word must be saved from blood and thunder.

When will I be able to rest on a breast with no scar? An absurd longing, from all points of view. An everlasting longing.

At that time I didn't know how to live or write. I had heard of dying. I was ignorant of what I didn't know. For example, I thought I knew how to read.

The unique moment arrives when you come in sight of the parting of the ways. A pitiless moment. When at last what had to happen, had to be written, is decided. You are going to have to choose. It is a particularly happy moment: because of the inevitable: what happens will be what had to happen. Therefore what has to happen has already happened. But you can't anticipate it. It is the moment about which you will be able to say afterwards: I knew it would happen like that. And that's the secret, the strangeness. How is it possible? If I knew? When I didn't know? It's that you can only come to it two ways. The one that goes left as you go out. And the other that seems to go right.

Obviously you can't go both ways at once, except if both of your selves think they are on the right road; or at least if one of you sets off earlier than the other; thinks it somehow may have an advantage, a start. And yet you are well aware that there are two ways. The strangest thing is that there is a third person and that's me, sometimes on one side, sometimes on the other, who is following all this. Who is for both runners at once. It is absolutely intolerable. And you wait for the moment when I-want and I-must-not are going to clash. While the first part of the race was on you were clearly on the side of I-want. When it seems that I-want will win, you can't prevent yourself from leaving I-want in the lurch. You wonder whether I-want has merely been used as pace-maker for I-must-not. There is no one to referee. Except me. These

134

quarrels can only be settled by force. You watch the row. So, one self will lose, you tell yourself. But as the loser you must want instant revenge. So there can't be a winner? You shouldn't have begun. Perhaps you just jumped in so that you could back out more easily?

To run away from the Present I turned left. When I came to the cross-roads I was surprised to see no one there. A nasty surprise. I must admit I had only ever run when I was sure of not getting anywhere. Where I was now, there was no loser to sacrifice. Except me.

I was in Tarshish like someone who had never left Nineveh. And yet I was alone. But like Jonah. Whenever you dream he is there. Wherever you draw breath you hear him. He was fixed in my breast. He was writing to me.

I fought. I was sincere. But I had been defeated long before, by my mothers, by my fathers.

When you wrote 'I fought' you never said a truer word. But I was fighting with the letters, I was beaten.

Recaptured. Stopped. Condemned to listen to them. They were strange, passing strange; terrible, more than terrible; they had absolute power over blood and mind. Terribly appealing and threatening. Who could have escaped them? No woman. Nothing could resist them. They would have captured me even if I had shut my eyes. As if it had been written that I would obey them. And each letter repeated that necessity. They read themselves to me without pity. They dragged me before him by force, into his story. I was the naughty pupil, the teacher was asking me to read; trembling I pronounced the words; the grand mineral words awoke my anguish, I was horror-struck. As soon as a letter referred to me a mist formed in front of my eyes. I felt myself summoned by the sentence that rejected me. They were relentless, open: no beginning, or end, no way in, no way out. They fell on me, or I fell into their bottomless space, with no safety net—I went on falling but the words held me up. I fell under their charm

135

which I loathed. Something was brewing. That's why I read them, to try to protect myself from them. To avoid their witchcraft. To shut them up, clip their wings. Cut off their sirens' tresses.

The truth is that I was wounded to the quick by the first letter and I had already caught god's madness.

And yet it was the only letter that I thought I was well-defended against: it had come from far away, for it was extremely close to him, from his most intimate naked self. Besides, it was naked. It began by: yes. *Oui. Ja.* I don't remember what language any more. As if I had asked him for something. And the letter was answering: yes. Yes. Here I am. Open mouthed. And I saw the tongue moving. As if you were asking god: are you there? And he said: yes, I'm here. In your mouth.

His affirmation. An intrusion. And he was naked in that letter. Brutally, he showed me what I shouldn't have seen. I opened it. I couldn't forget it. That morning it was very early. And it was written: 'Yes, I am in bed this morning, it is very early and I am naked.' As if he were lying on my bed; with me; but over there, and as if I was only dreaming I was here. I was disgusted by his nakedness, it took me by surprise. In my nakedness. It was an intolerable sight. I tore up the letter straightaway but the words had had time to escape, to creep into my blood and I was poisoned. It was an unusually long letter, he must have taken all night to write it, and in the end he exclaimed: 'Perhaps all this has just been an excuse to attract your attention and to snatch a smile. For why would I write to you as if you weren't here when you fill me so totally that there is hardly any room left for myself, not enough for my body, just enough for the first letter of my name. And it's now that you are calling me and I am forced to come to your call, at the very moment when no human being would be enough for me.'

I tore up the letter but the voice remained. It's the voice that persuaded me to read the second letter, the one that began with 'I don't want, I don't want, I have to come to you, when I am now only he who would have given you more . . .' The letter with the drawing that hurt me. I tore up the letter because of the drawing. I had hoped to blot it out, but it was graven forever.

It was such a peculiarly small sketch that I had to look very closely at it to make it out. At first I thought it was his initials entwined, or a Hebrew character. Actually it was a naked couple embracing; they seemed to be making love, creating themselves, tearing themselves away from each other to plant themselves again one in the other; they were coming to life, melting into one another till they turned into a single letter, and in the end this symbol plunged into the void.

I wanted to, I had to, tear it up. I couldn't; I had to try several times, the paper wouldn't be torn up. I took scissors and cut it up—because I had to.

I couldn't have touched the next letters without touching the body of the Present. They were written in such a way that they weren't letters any longer: I received moments, scenes, places, fragments of life, cities, flesh. No room for the paper. Walls, partitions, distance, envelopes were left out. He never protected himself. So how could I be spared? No eyelids left.

The voice had written: 'I will show you.' And it was true. He showed me. 'Come in.' I was inside. I saw his face in his voice. I had only ever written or received letters from the past, with news of the finite, from the point of view of the outside world. The Present wrote from his very blood, after the end had come, from new beginnings, from his marrow, his cells. He was very close to his core, very deep inside himself. And I was so far away from myself. He looked at himself in his sentences and smiled. His voice was all around me, limitless; answered me everywhere as if I had just spoken. There was no more silence for me.

*

137

Where is this vast, insatiable, everlasting suffering that is *me* going on? In the breast. In the room: in his breast. With the heart between the lungs. With dragons and lions. Now I understand—that the room was his body—I didn't realize it then. What I was living through then doesn't hurt the same parts of my body now. Today the seven blades are in my temples and the pain is in my memory—and I only recall myself dying.

My coming upset him: 'Wasn't the path steep enough? How jealous life is, it still betrayed you, deserted you just when you made up your mind not to regret it! Life wants to get the better of your last remaining strength. How late you came! And now here I am forbidden to sleep. The thought that when I am dead I won't see you any more, won't be able to love you any longer, stops me from lying down. The days to come will not be easy. That's why I am writing to you. The nights won't be any different either. The danger is that I might want to sleep to see you in my dreams and then I might not be able to wake up again.'

The Great Vigil began. He told me of the horror of having something living inside him. The terrifyingly unequal struggle: having to share his flesh and blood with the enemy, feed the enemy, carry the Other in his breast. He was the mother of his own death. I turned to him because I hated death.

He seemed to be waiting for a fateful day: 'I received a telegram: "Appointment in K the last day of the month. You are requested to arrive the day before." The order was not signed. Strangely, a few days ago, because there was no signature, I would have assumed that it was signed by death, but since you have come, I catch myself believing that it's signed by life. All I have to do to stop the Fiancé, to whom I am promised, from turning out to be the one I dread is to arrive on the last day still *on my feet*. That is why, H., as soon as I feel sleep creeping up on me, I begin to leap around the room, to throw it off. I am so light already that all I need is a page to hang on to, so that I can get up again. Provided that the page is meant for you.'

Day against night, hearing him build up his paper wall.

'How could I sleep?' As if I had asked him to lie down. And perhaps I had? Perhaps I was living, unawares, a life from which I was separated by bouts of sleep and cowardice. I began to be tired. Of running away. Of staying. Of lying in the bottom of the boat in a great storm, profoundly separate. Tired of hesitating.

You can use your ingenuity on your own behalf: bury yourself in a reading-room in Tarshish, climb up and down using your little step-ladder, reckon your future on your fingers, pump thin blooded books, feed on corpses, make your petty plans for life—like a blind man—take notes without pausing for breath, pretend to work. Cling to your fetters: prudence, caution, foresight, career, position. The books fell from my hands. The shelves caught fire. Instead of enriching myself with obsolete knowledge, I was losing my bearings. In the cave where I was sheltering in Tarshish I heard his voice as powerful as the divine breath that shatters mountains. How could you pretend that you weren't really in Nineveh?
'I don't understand what's happening to me, causing my inner conflict. Because of you I see myself coming to life at a time when I know I am dying. How could I fail to be disoriented, when I can't go forward or back?' 'And now I have found you I am lost as never before. Because I am no longer anywhere where you could, if you wished, meet me.'
Every letter told me: 'Climb up and look towards K.' Instead of climbing up I buried myself deeper down: I said over and over again: 'I can't see anything.' But going down like that exhausted me. Seven letters! And the voice insisted: 'Try again.' And the seventh time I did go up, and I looked.

Towards death. I thought I saw him disappear. He was sitting in the sun, his body sagging, his head in his hands, which were too thin, he had trouble lifting his head; as he did in his last letter. But he didn't write any more.

I sent a telegram: 'I can see it coming.' It was windy and raining heavily. I wept as if I had loved him.

If he had said to me: 'Come. Leave your story. And I'll tell you mine.' Perhaps I might have come. Perhaps I would have caught the first plane to Nineveh. At the last minute. Perhaps I would have caught the first plane to Paris. But he didn't ask for anything. That day the weather changed. The days got longer, the nights fell apart. I admitted the inadmissible. The letters came thick and fast.

I had trouble getting through them, because I was slow and mean-spirited. The flood of letters upset me, swept me away; I could measure my weakness by their strength. I spent all my time on them. They revealed inhuman strength. He was withdrawing all his Life's credit from his account, squandering dozens of years in a few weeks; becoming in a few weeks all the selves he could have been, risking everything, wrenching out the impossible. Only my own limitations prevented me from seeing his immense achievement. He was killing himself with Life. He said: 'Before the end of the month I'll have put all my lives in your hands, the ones I have known, the ones I might have known, and you will keep them alive. I won't leave until I have finished.'

He went on and on. Anyone else would have gone mad. He directed his history as if he were leading a people—and he himself was the people.

'We shall probably never live together. But you will live among all my people who have crossed the desert I am condemned to be.' I received his childhoods, I held them by the hand, the hair, the ears. I saw him in the streets of his native cities. I saw him lose his fathers, his first lands, his mothers. I saw him running without looking back, saw him disappear round corners. I wept. I read his reckless letters. I lost sight of him in all the countries that he would never return to—and was blinded by sorrow.

If I had ten bodies, ten lives I still couldn't contain the intensity of one of his thousands of stories. I met him every day of his past, followed him, loved him, lost him each day and found him again changed, in his next life. I never would have believed one single person could contain so many beings; I was swept away in the crowd. I saw him again: growing as he learnt, going through wars without flinching, taking frontiers in one bound, and conquering languages: mastering the languages of the North and the South or reading all the books. I saw his many faces in his letters, their young yet ancient, solemn beauty arrested in the past—I saw his smiles of a dreamer on death. All the battles he had fought, the mean actions he had hunted down, the evil he had torn to pieces, enemies of life run through—so that he rose just above humanity; just above human strength; frailty. I saw him drawing near to the great light, nearer than a human being should go, only to see himself halted one step from immortality, by death itself, and violently flung down. Even if I didn't love him, how could I fail to worship the man in his letters?

I was sitting in anguish at the top of the reading-room, the books I opened admonished me:

'We contain immense knowledge, but all our knowledge put together is a mere ludicrous babbling compared to what he knows.' My thoughts went tumbling down slopes, bannisters, stairs; they were the rats in my soul, the rats in my memory swarming out on all sides, deserting me as I followed the man in his letters. Not a rat, no child, no passionate young being could have resisted death's tune. Still today, when one single note of these letters sounds, by accident, a bar consisting of three words, even in a book that isn't dangerous, I am terrified by a nostalgic yearning. Because the wish to die

141

cannot die; only fear of losing myself compels me to refuse.

He used to sing me an eighteenth century *lied*: *Die Gedanken sind frei, wer kann sie erraten*. His voice didn't carry the words, it let them go, the words took flight, the voice grew gloomier, such light words, such a heavy voice. *Sie fliegen vorbei, wie nächtliche Schatten*. Such frivolous thoughts could stop them. *Kein Mensch kann sie wissen*. The voice insisted, the words were saved, given the chance of another life. Mine seemed worthless.

He had music, I had the rats.

My petty provisions routed, my ideas demolished; strength, thoughts, values scattered; all my trivial, painstaking attainments were too human; my history, my life reduced to dust. The mist that formed in front of my eyes when it was a question of me cleared as soon as he laid himself open to me: 'I will show you all the beings I have been.' Countless selves. Strange, passing strange, terribly appealing: his way of conjuring up out of the earth, out of texts, those who had preceded him in his fight against darkness. His way of reviving them; loving them sorrowfully, in terror; of making the voice of their last agonies re-echo in his voice; of gathering to himself alone the vast sum of their loneliness; their stores of knowledge. His anger since their deaths, angry unto death. I heard him set his name among the names of the betrayed. One day I heard him speaking in the booming voice of the Moor. I am black but comely. He was trembling with shame and hatred against He who had only fed him on honey from the lion in order to destroy him. I heard his voice merge into the frightful raging of the dying; at times letting only his own pain burst out in their songs, sometimes raising them from the dead with his really bitter words. As if he had had to rally all the powers of that kinship in anguish, gather together all their lamentations in his own breast, so that he could fling his true name against death.

And there were thousands of stories in his Parting Letters untold, as if all future books were going to die. Listen. Listen.

142

You were seeing Kafka vanish before he could write. You saw writing, languages, words, die with him. I listened and listened!

I joined him in the room the day I received the letter that ended like this: 'I still have a story to tell you, but I have a sore throat and can't talk any more.' It was June 5th. I was born on June 5th. and I knew that the story that couldn't be written was mine.

As soon as I opened the door my heart beat faster, my pulse raced, I couldn't speak. I entered the room as if I were entering his voice; entering my silence; to listen to him till the last word. Why you of all women? Why indeed; because there is no reason for anything.

Then you saw him uninterruptedly for the first time. You had never seen him before. You would never see him again, recognize him again—panic and grieving, yet again—Watch till the last day of the month. Report the day before—Don't eat—in K.

Close the door. Listen without fail for forty days, forty days and nights of your youth—pit the word against the Other. First the word, next sentences, then things. All the things that would not happen. Talk about what will never be. So that it may be. Gradually hear nothing but life murmuring, warm blood keeping you company. *Die Gedanken sind frei.* Time is dead, eternity watches over us. Saving one another from the abyss in the room. How far away the outside world was! Somewhere else. We were protected by the door.

Become him; adore him in his language. While he was telling us what could happen to us. Take the story of the Promised Life literally.

Under the white sheet, the prophesies he took lightly:

'—You would hate me if I died; if I were dead. That is why I won't die. What a job you've given me!' His teasing terrified me. Even if it were only half true. 'If I come back you'll find

143

me diminished. How could I find rest?' As if he were returning alone from *my* hells. His amazement tore me apart. 'Of all the stories I have told you the one that surprised me the most is the one that is carrying us away now, and I shall never be able to make up the end.'

And under the sheet the very breath of life.

'But the most astonishing thing that has ever happened to me is that we are lying beside one another, that I can touch you, despite the thing living inside me, and you are not disgusted.'

And I was surprised too, because I had stopped being myself and wanted to be him to the core.

There is no word in any living language to describe the violent intensity of a happiness being played out on the borders of death and eternity. But there is a word in the language of madness. To describe such Abominable happiness. Never yet lived by human beings. You see your life through the eyes of Moses when he was a hundred and twenty years old, in your prime at twenty-five, a god shows you everything you will never live to enjoy. Your future, the one you will never live. So that you enjoy it in the here and now.

A minute ago in the room it was yesterday, and a new day every moment; in a minute, tomorrow, you get up again and again, and every minute is today. I went into a cave to spend the last night and that night just wasn't going by.

Time in the room was not real time. The impossible was actually taking place. Carving days and generations out of the impossible, really living them: that's what happened. Every day was extraordinary, so many days in each look, so many events that they couldn't be recorded, no story could contain them without bursting. I have not forgotten anything. All the madness still burns in my memory.

In the room it was impossible to live as human beings do. But it was possible to live out the impossible, absolutely. The point was not to fall asleep. It was the Time of Times, eternity; all you had to do to live in it was to stay conscious.

144

Call each other, re-call each other, stay awake, keep life in sight. How to pass from one time to another, for thirty days and thirty nights and remain *present*.

I didn't make up the hotel. I remember its real name. We hardly ever went out. In real time, three trips to stock up. Those trips have been left outside, like dreams.

The bathroom was white. It was the place for our Journeys. Summer. Under water, imagine Africa, floating along the shores for days; we were light-hearted, like children together; above the water his voice which was too serious; his skin was extremely white, as if his body had been formed for a different light. The wide seas lay between us and death.

'I am not only the present. I can be the future, I'll prove it to you.' And it is true, still. The unique things that took place in the room have not disappeared. It was the second room, the one for births, journeys, marriages. The part of me that was there has never left. Almost the whole of this story has fallen back into time. It is preserved in my memory forever. Streets, gestures, clothes, shapes, stations, the hospital, monuments, newspapers. Even the letters have died. The thousand tapes lie silent.

But the Great Vigil has not vanished. It won't let me forget in peace. I never sleep: I come back to contemplate what is going to disappear . . .

Real life was going on *inside*. In those areas of Afterwards that I shall never manage to encompass in my writing; nor even to contemplate. Regions from which writing is exiled forever; like an exile which cannot give up hope of reaching the true city; which remains out of reach. Because the exile's fate is that of the madman who says to himself: 'If I could only get to Rome then I would be God the Almighty.' He tries with all his might to make the journey, to fulfil and not to fulfil all that the oracle pronounced. Perhaps one day he does reach the True City: there, the other life would begin and he would have to write the story of his New Self, but it can only be written in the language he doesn't know. Powers are keeping watch over my thoughts. But they could be tricked.

I took off in the room. Without reflecting or dreaming you wouldn't get into your inner journey. Despite the fear of falling ill. I didn't care. 'Do what is too difficult for you, in the aim of your re-search.' He pressed me. He had already let go. 'Come. My powers are not yours. I will show you all my strength and all my weakness, so you can see how I love you.' His confidence; he didn't get impatient easily. I was hesitating. Between shame and terror, my awe. I wasn't thinking, I was suffering: a little of that religious awe that primitive peoples felt when faced with the mad. What a coward I was!

'My head feels heavy; my arms leaden.' My wicked thoughts weighing down his lightness. I caused him all the trouble that ignorance causes truth. 'My thoughts are not your thoughts. But your distress is my pain.' I was sick of myself. I had him in my hand like the secret Letter; and because of my body I was so shy, so humanly animal and foolish; I was in his hand—alas, I wasn't even like a frightened bird. He opened his hand, said: 'fly!' I drew back, like a crab. within me was a merciless voice wounding me, crushing me with contempt. And yet I didn't give in to that voice. I gave in to him.

To his letter: 'The source of death's power lies in the caution of mortals.' Come. The wisdom of the *outside* is folly with me. I have read the Letter of Truth whose secret is madness. 'Come, let's go far far away—the entrance is here.' I found myself *inside* without knowing how. The minute before you were drawing back, calculating.

You reach the city. You were going to do an about turn, to go round it. Suddenly your mind is freed. And there you are, inside.

The sick have turned away from outer reality, which is precisely why they know so much about the inner. They

146

could reveal things which, without them, would remain impenetrable. But they've no reason to waste their time and blood for those who live outside, who prowl around like the shades in the Odyssey, hoping that one of the initiate will one day give them alms. Absurd hope. Those who are inside could not have got there unless they had broken completely with the outside. The strength that keeps them safe inside is the very strength that divides them completely from the shades. I went inside thanks to his illness. I had drawn the strength I needed from the blood of the man with the letters. From the very beginning I must have had a soul within me ready to speak the inner language. A mouth waiting to taste that life-blood.

I was deep inside. And now he was weary. But there were no more obstacles, nothing preventing me from going on. Step by step to the pure life. I was the Voice's daughter. He talked to me, I went forward; he told me tales, I learnt; he spoke to me, I desired; he sang the *lied*: '*Ich denke was ich will und was mich beglücket*,' he announced what he wanted and things obeyed. As if, now, nothing could stop him from achieving his ends.

He was here in front of me and lives sparked and rushed round him like moths to a flame.

I was enchanted; taken in. I would have lost myself completely but for my confusion, but for a flash of fear: the danger of going mad if I did or if I didn't take the next step. To go into the infinite all you need is the wish to get ahead of your fear. I learnt that.

Simultaneously you reach and don't reach the end and the beginning of time, in Cairo and in Jerusalem, the day before and the day after. If you want: reduce the universe to a space twenty paces to the North, twenty paces to the South and eight paces to the West. Get up in America, wash in Jordan, get to Rome in a flash avoiding the nine hundred and three doors of death. He wanted to. How could I not give in to such a will? Without going crazy with shame?

147

'One day, next year, in one year or another, I shall sleep in your arms.' Next year; the one that hasn't come yet.

I was totally trusting. Betrayal began. Perhaps then, or now even; perhaps somewhere else; in a passing thought; perhaps from the moment I entered the room? Who could say how it got in? Through what soul-lapse?

The room was full of his stories. How could I betray him? It wasn't even me. I could never get over him. I believed everything he said. Trusting, I went with him into his cities of nostalgia: where there was no room for me. He painted them in words and I saw them.

He had decided to go 'right up to the pure marble steps,' which only very pure, very light unattached beings have a chance of reaching. I was heavy as lead, unclean, a mass of contradictions. And besides, I didn't even know where the marble steps were; no one had ever told me about them. He reached them through the power of his in-sight. Fighting against darkness. When he started out everything was opaque, closed. You had to be mad to hope to carve a way through all that nothingness. He succeeded through dream flashes. Instead of falling asleep he plunged violently into sleep like a knife stabbing. In terror I watched him doing it: suddenly he withdrew into himself, there was another world inside his body: limitless, airy depths that he had to cross at the risk of being crushed. His tough, tense body went slack during this acrobatic feat, he crossed over an abyss which was mirrored in his face, he recovered after a minute which seemed an eternity, during which time I had lost him. I had seen him fall, turn pale, disappear, leaving me behind—and I was the one who was dying.

When he returned he would tell me all about it, word by word, step by step—it would take hours. The minute had been torn free from any laws. Time as another space. I wouldn't have got over it, even in an ordinary room. He gave

148

me texts from the *inside* to listen to. What emerged spontaneously had the formal beauty of a work of art ten times reworked. As if through these trips he went back to his origins in the Book. He became the immortal child of the Word.

He went on speaking, moved on, kept on reporting, went so far beyond the unreal cities, approached the inner, came close to the secret, grasped life with words and told me the words.

I didn't say that I didn't talk then, because things were unsaid in another world of which I had no knowledge, to which I never returned. Why pay any attention to my deficiencies and failings? You don't have to take any notice of what isn't even there. I kept quiet, I smiled: 'Your smile brings on the night. Brings on yesterday. A different yesterday from yesterday, the yesterday that will be today.' His voice went straight to my breast, to the heart which is the *inner* ear. His voice was my life's blood. The touch of his skin brought me to life.

One wall did not topple. There was an immurement which I forgot.

Because he had made up his mind, he could live on life, nothing but life. His will was really inflexible; absolute authority. Every organ obeyed. No deflection. Each thought went straight home, not an atom of life was lost. He was totally concentrated. How could I admit to someone so centered how scattered I was? When you have shut yourself up in the room, closer than the dead in their place, you have broken all ties, *die Gedanken sind frei*, and the most distant visions appear to you in mirages, your thoughts lead you into long forgotten lands: there you are in your native land, on the other side of the world, there you are going down South along desert tracks seeking nothing in meaningless space—it is as if the outside world was breaking out in the most exterior images possible to confirm just how absurdly exterior it is. And you are wretched and ashamed as you see yourself being

149

swept so far away from your own flesh and blood for such incongruous scenes.

A spirit is persecuting you. Why reward its wickedness by taking notice of it? When I wanted to be absorbed, centred.

A whole week without eating. My body was striving to imitate his; to share his power. I was hungry. I kept my hunger to myself. I was obsessed with the thought of pancakes and honey; humiliated by it. A secret craving. *Mein Wunsch und Begehren kann niemand verwehren.* It was feeding off what I was repressing. I didn't want the Thought: 'If he slept I would go down to the nearest café.' I was afraid of thinking, of feeling the thought trying to take shape in a dark corner of my body, putting the words together, climbing up my stairs, reaching my door, knocking for me. Before the thought manages to get itself recognized take it by the throat, strangle it, let it out, vomit it up. I didn't want to admit to myself that the thought must have taken advantage of a certain complicity; I am the victim, dragged through the body, kill me; just a hint of a thought; I didn't want to think; '*I* didn't think that.' Every minute, shuddering with disgust, I leapt over embryos, larvae, a tangle of evil spirits. Nothing is forcing you to react. Ignore them; ignore yourself. Get away from the enemy. You struggle to tear yourself free of the laws of nature— your body had never been such a danger to you. It's not up to me. You are a prey to your organs. Don't fight. It's a trap. Fight. It's a trap. Hesitating every minute. Nothing wrong with that. You are not the one who makes the laws, it's your stomach that's upset. You are exposed to a combination of bad nerves and jealousy. There is someone inside your body, a thing, a beast, jaws tearing at you; it's the body itself making other bodies. The whole day long you quell it, fear it. Refuse to listen to it. Forget it. Act as if it isn't taking its revenge. Let it speak: 'Three pancakes with maple syrup.' What a trite trick! Almost too low, too banal. Your stomach think's it's you.

Don't listen to it. You didn't have the thought. Pretend it never occurred to you.

I had more important things to do than defend myself against insubstantial phantoms.

Listen to him. I listened to him. Almost all the reverberations have died down now. My pulse is no longer racing, I say his names without trembling, I have forgotten some of them; streets and addresses have vanished, even the language has gone. His voice hasn't. His voice weighed against my silence; I listened to it; I couldn't hear myself. I can still hear the room echoing with his naked song, powerful, weighty, bewitching. No room in the world for my silence which I never thought about.

Without eating, almost without drinking; unwilling; beside him in the womb; and yet you are in another world sometimes, unawares; with no story; no sleep; never leaving him; you are in the song, nearer and nearer to him; and yet I was never so separate; so separate that you never felt it; as if the separation was going on behind your back; beyond you; or as if separation was splitting from itself; wasn't splitting you but taking you in. And I couldn't bear it.

Little by little a pane of glass formed.

My lack of frankness: no time to analyse it, admit it, notice it. His sentence: 'And one day, in one year or ten, I shall lie quiet in your arms'—split me in two. If I went outside the room I became distraught, weak, a year opened out in front of me, I collapsed, the Promised Day vanished. He would never make it. At that thought I shut myself up in the moment, with no memory, no imagination. I plunged into the abyss of the bed, under the sheets, between his legs, so that fear would pass over without touching me. While fear hovered round without getting at me I listened to his words and rejoiced. I was unfaithful in good faith: I believed he wasn't thinking of K any more, instead of waiting for the day he would be silent, I was lying quietly between his legs, against him. Believing he had forgotten the day of reckoning. Not believing, not thinking, not reflecting, avoiding any questions, any selfish emotion—while I had it out with myself. Rejoicing silently when I saw him coming nearer to his time and not thinking about it.

Not asking yourself whether someone deep down inside you was not wanting him to be spared from death; to spare you. Since I didn't want to be away from him for a second. You didn't suspect you were deluding yourself, as if adoring him was enough to assure you he was telling the truth. This wasn't merely foolish; it was a trap. I wasn't wrong. There was no right or wrong. He said 'I will be silent.' What he desired was law. 'I shall lie quiet in your arms. One day.' And that day would come. What did I care about the future, past words, the delay, the wait; I wasn't waiting for anything, the year would go by, the moment would turn back on itself; reality had nothing to do with truth. What he announced was true in advance. Don't argue, trust. If you don't believe trust anyway. I believed; I thought I believed. And you are haunted by truth, you can feel its breath, you know what it wants of you. I don't turn round.

You wouldn't accept it, even if it were true. For him the truth was that he no longer wanted to die, and everything would turn out as he decided. Even if he were going to die. In reality, truth was merely stupid and trite. His truth was so noble that it could not be undermined by error. It didn't need to be verified. In silence love him as myself; betray him. While I was continually thinking about K, not telling him; I implicitly attributed my blindness to him.

Don't let him see himself: as if there was no room; no-body; no K; no threat; no battle; no reality. While I lived each hour as if it were his last, I lived the same hour with him, in silence; not in the room, nor outside, in Egypt standing leaning against his chest in front of a sphinx that I tried to contemplate through the eyes of his secret. While the Vigil split me in two.

So that all the immortal wishes of his childhood would come true. Mine wouldn't come true at the same time, but I didn't count.

You tried to do what was too difficult for you. You didn't succeed. Did you want to be an angel with four faces, continually on the look out, with eyes in the back of your head, never sitting down? I was too tired.

Without lying, without hiding, without a break, caught between his desires, in his arms, the things I didn't say, that I forgot; weren't forgotten; remained, ignored; as if he could fail to hear what I didn't say; before my silence. I never realized that I didn't have anything to hide because I didn't have anything to say: he had already seen right through me. I was so far away from myself that I didn't know what I knew. I didn't open my mouth. Something was terrorizing me. Not in the name of terror. In the name of joy in terror. I dreaded using a distressing intonation. Such a shameful thing can happen so easily. His life hung by a word.

I was continually saying to myself in the past-present tense: 'Yesterday, he is watching me and I am watching him seeing me.' We are locked in a death struggle. 'Never before' turning into 'Never more'. Although I didn't catch myself parting us, a bloody separation was taking place; I tried not to notice it. Splitting yourself in two; I went from one self to the other without any continuity. I was inside the split as I was inside silence, between his sheets—not feeling it.

The thought: 'Yesterday, everything is here today as if nothing could happen to us,' evoked the other thought: 'the secret of an everlasting day: take a little time and make up years and years. And in the mean time rest. The present is expanding.'

From hour to hour a pane of glass formed. It doesn't stop you reflecting. I had no reflection.

Denn meine Gedanken zerreissen die Schranken und Mauern entzwei. Die Gedanken sind frei.

Instead of having a conversation, listen to him sentence by sentence, till you go mad: the next will be the last, strain your ears, hear his voice echoing in the lost present, try and hold on to his voice, fearing to hear the last word explode in every sentence; don't listen for it any more, lie in wait for it, greedily. If only I could jot them down. Fight the temptation; unsuccessfully; the shame of wanting to hang on; as if he were no longer living; the shame of discovering that you are greedy. In the bathroom, wishing: 'If only I had a pencil I'd use it. To pin down a word on a scrap of paper.' Not daring to do anything: the door wasn't shut. 'Close the door and do it quickly.' I couldn't. I left it ajar.

You are constantly fighting off the fear: 'it's the last, you'll be sorry;' the temptation 'You'll hate yourself later.' And you find yourself in the bathroom again, repeating the last sentence to yourself, irresistibly moved by an impulse of love, of betrayal. Don't note anything. Remember on the sly. You *are* memory. In the toilet, behind the door, without losing a word, I fancied I was getting closer to him. Don't take your eyes off him through the crack. Four faces to gaze on god. The sentences I remembered plunged me into mourning. As if it were all over. You are a shameful memory. Alone, pretending you want to go to the bathroom, repeating the morning's first words to yourself. Hang on to them. Grab hold of them. What a predator you are. Gobble up everything he said. And what if someone had said to me: 'Are you stocking up for the future?' But there was no one there. I wasn't keeping watch on myself. Fear was feeding off itself. I was put aside till later. If the sentence ending with 'before killing him off' had been uttered in full I would have died of humiliation. Something was stopping it taking shape. I needed to forget. At all costs.

—Isn't he still alive?—If you say that it means he is already dead.—Trust.—I do trust. On and off. All the time. Under pressure. Hurt. But intermittently.—If you say: I do trust, you are doubting. Don't say that.

Before killing him off.

I must keep the door ajar. So that nothing can happen. So I can trust completely. I want to grasp the separation.

All the sentences I have suppressed haven't stopped hurting me, imprisoning me in their letters for ten years.

154

'What amazes me is that I don't believe anything will happen now. Whatever happens. I reached you.'

'It is impossible to live where there's no room to sleep, where I can't delude myself by saying: I am at home here. And yet I am living like that without rest, without self-deception, because you are here, I am at home.'

Your words are not my words. They are not just words.

'Everything is turning out as if I had previously written everything that has brought us here. And from now on I am taking my pleasure—it's got nothing to do with writing now.'

'I completely forget myself. As if I could forget myself without losing myself. I won't sink into oblivion. I have gone so deep into you.'

The sense of these words still draws me, lures me away from myself, out into infinite space. They still hold my attention; gradually forming, growing, teeming inside me. Capturing my attention, dragging me along—beyond ignorance and knowledge—into his desires, into his foreign languages.

'*I have become the daring young man on the flying trapeze.* My life requires me to outstrip time, every second. In-between-time nothing can happen. Perhaps you yourself are the trapeze. But sometimes I think you are the air in which I find no rest.'

Sucked into their promises, their threats.

'What is soothing about life is that it hangs, literally, by a word. *Ruft man sie mit dem richtigen Wort, dann kommt sie.* That is also what is frightening about it. There are countless different accidents lying in wait for the word.'

His words still ensnare me; hold me up; disconcert me: Silence me.

'I haven't just turned into an acrobat. I already was one when I used to write.'

I am still enmeshed in their witticisms and innuendoes.

'I don't need to call her any more! Now it's she who is calling me. She is the one who is afraid of losing me!'

'Call me! Call me by my name. And I'll be there.'

Extraordinary, fatal joy. To begin calling all over again,

every moment. 'Are you there?' 'Yes.' Him again. There again.

'You will tell me: everything.'

His words still heavy on my breast. The weight of their assurance hurt me, reassured me.

'Afterwards, you will be able to tell me everything you can't say to me now.'

And yet I thought I was telling him everything; had told him everything, as never before. I was frightened by the word 'everything'—luckily it has been swept away by time; or, what comes to the same thing, everything I had not said keeps me so far away from 'everything' that I wasn't any the wiser. I didn't think I had hidden anything. Or had anything to hide, because I was really less than nothing.

A sentence brushed past me, I started:

'When you listen to me like that I wonder how the outside is affecting what you hear. It can't be by chance that I don't dare ask you where you are. You must be in the secret.'

It didn't touch me. It was probably just a feeling.

'Promise not to be angry with me. If you don't blame me here, you will once you are outside. Don't blame me. And then, if you want to hurt me, don't. I don't want you to hurt yourself.'

If you don't understand, trust, don't blame anyone else.

'Do you understand me? Impossible.'

Always on edge, not understanding. This isn't the time to try. There were sentences hidden within his sentences.

'All this is to notify you: I am talking to you, I am here.'

Sometimes I didn't understand, other times I thought I did; something in his voice must have caused me pain: a reproachful tone underneath his triumphant voice. And yet you must know there's never any blame.

'You won't suffer. Tell yourself that if you are suffering I shall suffer.' I told myself that.

His assertions were compelling. My doubts no longer raised their voice above these blasts. They wouldn't have carried any weight. They barely managed to keep going, they petered out. Because of his inner confidence. Unnoticed, they were piling up meanwhile between the bed and the bathroom. No thicker than mist. Half there, half not—like me. And so insubstantial. I forgot. There was a truce. The room was so peaceful. I thought it was peace-time. 'My soul is kept quiet like a child beside its mother.' I wasn't roused by impatience.

'What, where, how, why? I would like to know. Where from and, above all, when? I would like to know. I know everything. But there is a fearful lot left, vast as time, as my life. You didn't tell me where you come from *in me*, where you come from *for yourself, against me.* You don't answer anything. You don't answer any of those questions.'

The questions didn't upset me; I didn't think they were really questions—just the dust of his desire thrown in my face. The child rubbing up against its mother's dress. That's what you thought. Amazement echoing and re-echoing. Everything was so discrete. I didn't feel the questions were really asking anything of me. Not really. That's why I didn't answer. They were rhetorical. That's what you told yourself. That's how I answered. The peace weighed heavy. The mist thickened. I didn't see what was coming.

'When you look at me in silence I get the feeling that you can see something coming. As if you were looking 'afterwards.' At the same time I think I am wrong. If there were something, she wouldn't hide it from me.'

I wasn't forced to take it up. The feeling would go away. Love had answered in advance, the details were unimportant. Talking would have brought me back to him; deaf to the essential. My silence couldn't be heard.

—His words coming at you like thunder clouds, can't you see something brewing?

Your confidence is suspect. Why should I be suspicious? why torture myself?—That's for you to say.—Am I deluding myself? He always has the truth on his side. And you are on

157

his side too. As if there were no one in your place.—You know I'll believe you. I wasn't going to suggest anything.—A little doubt had crept through his words. Faded away. Before I could put a name to it. A vague suspicion was registered. I would have been ashamed to admit it. Just a little weariness. A strain in the eyes.

A lull, that ought to warn you that now is not the time to ask yourself questions; ignore suggestions; with hesitation. I wasn't noting. I was learning. My soul had been commandeered. 'Is it because of me?' That question couldn't have reached me. Anywhere. I was absolutely preoccupied by the fear of not grasping him. I wasn't myself. And if you had been on your guard? The peace might have alerted you.

There were the dreams of silence: it all started with a call; inaudible; perhaps it was in his dreams, he felt himself being dragged out of a black sleep; or perhaps it all began with his expecting a call. When he had reached the right place. It would be decisive. The thing happened in a minute, one everlasting night.

And so there were two calls; or the same one breaking the silence. Everything was made of silence. Night, space, streets, his body hewn out of the same immoveable substance. To be got through. A lifeless silent night was resisting him, like the silence that resisted his questions; a void weighing heavily, an icy resistance against which he had to keep on pressing his body of silence; a cruel thing to be repulsed at every step, an invisible fabric woven over and over again, so that it took years to wear out. Then the call, the real one, reached him. When he no longer had the strength to listen to it. Scarcely the strength to notice the din, which must have been prodigious, since it was heard by a dead man. Because, if the call had such trouble reaching him, it meant that he had just died. And he told me over and over again how horrible it was

158

to run across the never-ending street—till he came to his corpse. Without ever meeting anyone.

'I am more and more alone. What do you do when I turn my head? Don't forget me when I close my eyes. I won't be a minute.' I protested, sincerely.

'These dreams don't come from me. I know you don't forget me. I am not being unfair. And yet, I am forgotten.'

His way of telling you: 'I can see crowds all round you. Do you think it's an illusion?—and he wasn't joking. I might have been frightened if I hadn't been so sure of being as close as I could possibly be to him. I swore it was an illusion.

'I believe you. You know I trust you. But how do you explain this: I shut my eyes. It was the first time I had managed to beat the night. I was standing before the steps. Day was dawning. One more step and the silence would be broken. I was about to hear the voice calling: the call that would put an end to the silence. I knew it would be your true name, or my name for afterwards. I wasn't asleep. Why was it that moment of all moments that you began to call me, as if I wasn't there? Your voice stopped me hearing the name, I felt it going away—as I was struggling to seize it something broke in my breast.'

How could I explain what had never happened? He had said: 'Wait for me. I'll be back.' I had waited for him without moving, without saying a word. It wasn't I who cried out. No one had.

'Even if it were a dream, it was your voice. Even in my dream it was you who stopped me. What should you have said to me?'

Nothing. I was bowled over by dread: I had been flung out of eternity into the deadly present, without knowing how I had fallen. Not here. Not far from here. At fault, without even knowing it. I could tell by his sorrow. You have been running to meet him for months, from way back in the past; nothing could stop you—the gap remains: as if you were rushing towards distance in person.

159

'—You must know where you are. Answer me, please.'
What word could I utter when I had become distance itself.
Where are you? The simplest, the most complicated words
were turning inside out, splitting apart. I didn't understand
anything any more. I was afraid of trapping the words, afraid
of not saying them. Afraid of not calling truth by the name
that calls it out. Despite my passionate longing to have
something to say. Didn't you have anything in reserve then?
Nothing good. *Nichts Böses.*—What could have separated you?
Nothing but the dust his desire raised and the door that
doesn't shut. Is that where the split took place? Between the
bed and the privacy of the bathroom?

—A detail of no interest.—How can you be the judge of
that? I would be ashamed to think about it. Ridiculous
feelings; they're not worth noting. Such a slight movement of
withdrawal, a tremor at the most; a twitch of the eyelids.
Nothing could be more insignificant.

It was in the bathroom. I had completely forgotten it. The
room was private, familiar, hidden from observation. A home
with no ghosts. A feeling of uneasiness arose, faded away. I
didn't worry about it. I don't remember where it came
from.

It remained vague, during the conversation. He was
talking to me in German. I needed all my concentration. I
listened to him with all my senses. It was a question of a
quotation: '*Besser zu durchdenken.*' He was anxious to give it to
me to think over. The quotation wouldn't come, escaped
him, irritated him, needed coaxing. Smiling, he persisted. He
was sitting on the lavatory seat. Where did the resistance
come from? I might have been a bit tense. I would have liked
to be able to help him. 'I'll get it. It'll come.' I was probably
making something out of nothing: and what if his memory
were failing? I had the painful intuition that he was being
attacked from inside. You became impatient. For him. His
desires were my desires.

'*Ich glaube nicht dass es Leute gibt, deren Lage ähnlich der meinen ist.*'

Imagine the inner conflict.

I imagined the situation. It upset me. I sensed an ambiguity. In a way I was hesitating. Perhaps I should have gone away. Out of discretion, modesty. Actually, I had never seen a man in labour.

Right in front of you. Relieving himself, of life, of death, of separation. Talking to me all the while as if he were having a conversation with himself; with his body.

'What fascinates me is the way my body resists me, forcing me to live. The only part of myself that I approach without being able to say in advance that I have it under control. If I crack up—I mean the part of me that fancies it makes the decisions—the body never fails to remind me of itself. I say: I, a lie: I am dependent on my obstinate body.

I was standing in front of him; attentive; split. Actually I would rather have gone out. But I couldn't want that.

'I still have a few beautiful little things left to create which will outlive this carnage.' His serenity, my agitation, his ease, my heart beating to the rhythm of his reflections. 'The things I used to create always had something to do with paper, pen, typewriter, envelope, fiction. I personally told myself that I wouldn't write any more; to hang on had become meaningless. My body thinks otherwise. It is behaving like a patient mother with her naughty child.'

He was giving me a lesson. Like a mother. I had trouble taking it in. Anguish was stirring. I saw him without looking at him. He, personally. On the lavatory seat. Without shutting my eyes, try not to see him. And yet you were delighted. I didn't know where to put myself. He sitting serenely in the bathroom.

'As if the body had to re-educate me. It won't let me get away. It retaliates. If I didn't have that child I would be dying every second. What a job it has; what a job I have!'

I was identifying with him; his lack of shame delighted me;

the simplicity of the out-law; mimic the intestinal contractions to bring him on—you couldn't do it. I began to feel shame, I couldn't get rid of it. I was untrained.

His way of getting it over with: affirming a sense that couldn't be faulted. Exclaiming '*Das ist schön.*' The quotation came out. Like a love letter, defecation, affirming a presence in separation, despite absence. Separation doesn't split you in two. His relief '*Das ist schön*!' A birth re-enacted: memory restored. 'This production is a resurrection. I was buried between life and death. Just as I was getting frightened, the scene was revealed.' It was a final scene, he recited it to me very fast; so he had always known it by heart, pushed it away, held on to it, played it over and over again. 'The poet was about to die—*Raabe im Sterben*: in death: *als ihm seine Frau über die Stirn strich*—while his wife stroked his brow: '*Das ist schön.*' '*A nice crap.*'

That scene hurt me. That's lovely. In death, where death was put aside, overcome, left out.

In front of him, turning away—imperceptibly. I noticed:

The spacious bathroom with no windows was white; bath, wash basin, toilet, tiles, towels—were all white.

That couldn't have been at all significant.

—Where were you?—Beside him, between your legs, on the bed, inside *still-life.*—And yet I can feel you breathing as if you were coming back; to yourself, perhaps; from very far away; and I just felt completely alone—I was here.—I sense it in the rhythm of your blood. You are going to hate me for loving you so attentively.

Sometimes I had a vague fear of starting to be afraid. How could I have explained something so absurd, so vague?

'Everything you think is important.' If he'd known! He will never know where you were, and neither will you.

Fear of stroking his brow; afraid of that fear; afraid I would let him suspect my fear.

I have become the fear of myself.

His activity, my dread, my vacillation, my resistance.— 'Am I mistaken?' He wasn't mistaken. He was being mis-taken. I was mis-taken too.

The room was like a mad house. What are you doing there? Don't you know what you're in for? Yes, no. When you're not ill you don't stay in hospital for the fun of it. And it is not even a real hospital, it's the essence of a hospital. The room was agonizingly filled with absence; all was vanity. The bed that you were lying on was huge and dismal. What are you doing there? I am forgetting myself; letting myself go numb till I disappear completely. I am there and not there. No more decisions. Passive. In a torpor I abolish time. Regressing. I am far away, I am beside myself.

I lay quiet in his arms. How much longer? Another week; till the last minute. Nothing had happened yet. Such a slight feeling of unease, just enough to breach the peace.

How did he see you? Despite your absence, silence, your mind wandering even when he was kissing me. I can't imagine. His All-Presence was enough. Did you think you were there? How calm everything was, in terror, and joy was trembling at the heart of the anguish that doesn't crush it but contains it. In his arms, and no room for an outside.

Huddled against him, throw out again: 'Are you there?' 'Yes.' 'Are you there?' 'I'm here.' He was the one who was there.

It is impossible for the child to understand the love of which he is the object. The loneliness of the person he will never have known. Think only of him, just be one of his thoughts, until *you* disappear.

*

Beside him, so peaceful—like being at home; in the closeness
in which distance takes root.

—Is there anything else you haven't said? Trifles? Some bit of
smut that's dirtying the glass pane?
   —No. The only things I haven't said have really nothing to
do with us. The usual flaws in the memory—everyone has
them.
   That's one way of putting it.

—Is there anything trivial, anything crucial that you haven't
dared tell? No. No.—While he was caressing you?
   Under the sheet, in the tent of forever, his head between
your thighs.
   Everything comes back, the years turned on me and threw
the most repulsive shameful, unbearable things back at me.
   His tongue on the silky hair round your clitoris, I endured
it—Take me, his light mouth on your lips, lick me—I'm
closing my eyes so you can watch me,—slide behind my eyes.
   In memory's mansion, one of those buildings that are so
empty and calm and so vacant that they hold a fatal
attraction for your ghosts, there is a bit of something rotten, a
bit of dead life, to stir them up, while he slid between your lips
and called to you, Come, and possessed you, *Come*, *Come*, and
trusted you as ever.
   There was the dream of The Coming. The moment of
absolute anguish that woke him up.
   'Reality had never seemed so real to me. I was in bed;
absent from myself. In the dark. Literally inside darkness. It
wasn't a dream. I was lying down, as if I were someone else.
But the bed had moved slightly. The moment was approaching in person. And I didn't exist; my strength had deserted
me. A noise woke me up—I had gone.
   'I was suddenly so afraid that I couldn't even be "frightened." I was already gripped, distraught. I was awake and yet
not awake. When I woke I couldn't wake up. I was lying here.

It really was happening to me. I had heard the click of the door. Sharp, short, terrifying. What had to happen was happening. I woke up (too late). How could I have woken up? It, was really impossible to *live* what was happening. Death, which never 'happens' to anyone, was 'happening' to me. I wasn't thinking it in my dream, I was living it, it wasn't a dream. I was in this bed. I knew. It was the end, the absolute end. Mine: as if death couldn't come to me unless I were awake. I would be spared nothing. You shall not sleep. You will feel me coming. You will have no defence. You will live me. Who opened the door? It wasn't even someone. The moment approached, the inescapable. It wasn't the same room any more. I knew I was 'somewhere else.' In what city? I wasn't in a city. I was really somewhere else: this somewhere else existed because there was nowhere else for me to be any more. It wasn't the same bed; but it was me. I could hear it: nameless, black, coming on. If only it could have come while I was asleep! My body melted into the bed which merged endlessly into formless space. And it was no longer my body either: I was the darkness, with no arms, no legs, no body, extending into the thick air, motionless. My head was left, motionless, conscious. I was paralysed. I had the crazy urge to make a gesture; to separate myself from the boundless black weight which was swallowing up the bed, room, door, corridor, staircase, building. Everything was black and heavy in the dark and the darkness was hurling itself into the earth to which I had returned. Or rather: the earth had risen up and engulfed me. I was dying of fright. The Coming—what pain! Blind, unable to move. I was tortured by one thought: 'If you hadn't been alone this wouldn't have happened.' Do you understand? I wouldn't have died of anguish in the dark. I wouldn't have lived this. If I hadn't been completely alone. And while the endless thing continued to approach I vaguely imagined that a masculine being would come in; who was taking an atrociously long, atrociously short time to come the short distance down the corridor; because of all the suffering and paralysis piled up between the other and the bed. I got up in the end, I'm sure, I was standing up, completely alone in the room. I had managed it then; it was ludicrous; I hadn't managed to wake up, the darkness was still there. Put out an arm? What for? I lay down again. I felt that dying on your feet must be more painful. Waiting to be touched. The invisible leaned over. I waited till the last second and grabbed hold of it: by the neck, the shoulders. With deadly loathing. And that skin, those arms, the neck—were you. Not really you: what you were for me, here. But still you, and I felt sorry I couldn't tell you what had just happened to me. The unique pain of having lost the way back. Why wasn't it really you? Why wasn't the bed in it's place?'

For a long, long time, he, lying beside me, without touching me, I, not daring to touch him, he couldn't get back to himself—his rigid body paralysed me. Such harsh suffering. 'My love, what have you done to me? You shouldn't have left me, even in my dream.' His sorrow hurt me. 'Do you think I am being unkind?'—No, no. 'I said to myself in the dark: there is no one there. How could you have been so careless! To be completely alone; with no one. It's only then that the end can come. Do you understand? There was already *no one* there. I was *already* absolutely alone.'

Did you understand? Not really.

At that time, (the time of the second room), I still had not felt terror in love. I never could have imagined what would follow. Worshipping the Worst. Slip between the sheets, god the mother's dress smells so good; if only you could stop growing up, if only you could stop that night and not die, instead of waking up—mad.

Drowsy, so peaceful, until the day fixed for K.; with no fear, no trembling, inside love's soothing disquiet. Turned inwards, inside, with no connection to an outside. Where the abyss was deepening.

166

Treacherous reality was outside. A vast black land in ferment, its waves surging right up to the building, the hotel was in danger. My soul was safe like a child in its mother. The window stayed closed.

Go out of the room on October 10th, go down into the street, *I'll be back*, drinking-in his voice, eating up his words, *while I'm there*, not living, not dying, melting into him, *create us*; a taxi stopped, no arms, no legs, no flesh and blood, through the back window, his smile did not fade.

The world was in ruins, seas swept in, cities huddled together, traffic swooped in, wars broke out, countries rose in revolt, there was universal unrest. His face turned towards me. I would never go to K. The outside stayed outside.

How simple were the sorrows that followed! How beautiful were the fears, every day his day, during the months of terror: he in K, me somewhere where I was not. Luminous anguish. In his Smile. From one letter to another, death, life, letter after letter.

And between two letters, the surgical knives, the chest cut open, lungs laid bare, behind the shutters, the theft of blood, white hands round the heart, a vulture hovering over his head, violation of the divine, rape of the depths of his being. One bloody chance in a hundred to come out alive. He said: 'I'll be back.' The operation. An Illusion? Between the breasts.

All is true. Illusions, projections, death-struggle, wounded lungs, heart failure; secretions of the flesh and of distance. All false? It's true that only truths, beliefs when nothing happens, are absolutely personally true: love, life, what doesn't come, what is, what doesn't happen, what you can't tell yourself; death. All the rest is lies. For months, from one day to the next, distraught, from one fear to the next, being here in the 'never more' while your 'now' is risking its life at a distance, where your blood is being shed drop by drop, five thousand miles away. Until the Promised End: the driving out of death; fear follows fear, they are fighting for your life, 'in another country'.—Where are you?—My soul is in a hospital waiting-room which I have never set foot in; my body confined in the last dress, the one I was living in on the 10th October, when I was still looked at; a summer dress that I wasn't wearing any longer, rather it was wearing (out) my body from one fear to the next terror. In the house of Sorrow and Suspense. I was living there with myself as if with another person; living in the large unquiet house with anguish itself. We had been having this amicable conversation together, forever. *Angst* and I. The orange dress was wearing me (out). Not eating for days at a time. At the window, look towards K, forty days and forty nights and all the waters of the vast abyss had swallowed up the earth. Everything I had known had died away. Amnesia increased and grew fat; I was floating above myself; all the creatures in my life vanished; my body was inside the dress, far from mankind; far from all the men in my story—from brother to brute.

Shut in the room at the top: through walls, over frontiers, through tempests, ocean winds, above the noise of peoples, bombings, over the silence of the beings who had been quickened by the breath of my life—straining my ears to catch each one of my heart beats. Not eating if he wasn't—he was being fed by tubes. Someone had put some orange juice outside my front door. I would have been blinded by the sight of anyone else's face but His. There was only room for him, and what was for him, in my ark. I forgot, forgot, everything that wasn't to do with him; tortured me, made me sick. It was the Great Evacuation.

All familiar surroundings turned brutally alien. I was in the house as if in a nightmare, with a constant feeling I was being driven out—Out—Out—absolutely unbearable: impossible to find shelter, peace, a quiet corner which no sound that didn't come from him wouldn't shatter. Turned inwards, more and more, but inside an outside which was more and more violent, more and more repellent. More and more inside herself, with him, but exiled, under attack. Amnesia doubled its powers. Immobility. Concentration. Evacuation. Despite resistance and reproach. I shall come to you without ancestors, without descendants.

Her craving to be cut off, to be deep inside him; not to be approached, touched, threatened by a presence, a voice, a letter, a single hair. If your mother writes to you, send the letter back unopened. If someone says your name, don't hear it, don't take any notice of it, it is not your name, it is not his voice. If your mother speaks to you, cut her off. Send the following telegram: 'Don't come. I'm alive. Carry on as if I had left.' And this one, straight after: 'Don't come near me. You'll be sorry if you do.'

The passionate urge not to hold on to anything, anyone; not to be touched by anything, in any sense. To be freed from all ties. Isolate yourself in order to accomplish this. Go out at night, barefoot, go down stairs (—each step is a wrench— when no one is on the look out, creep in the dark up to the waste land and fling the past into it; night after night: remains, papers, the contents of your drawers, photos, notebooks, tainted objects) purge space—whatever you do isn't enough —the enemy has crept in, even into the wall-paper, everything is filthy, you'd have to burn the lot. The weight of the furniture stopped you breathing. Get rid of it.

Strip yourself, cast off false goods, break contracts; if the world lays a finger on you, cut it off; cut loose, burn your boats, only keep uncertainty for yourself, so that you can devote yourself exclusively to him. Cut off your old allowance.

Withdraw from the outside world. Walk in passion among flames. Shake off helping hands, refuse to let the past in. Close accounts, doors, gates.

Simplify, cut away, cease to produce, to barter; resign, reduce the six hundred and thirteen commandments to naught. Instead of teaching, learn how to lose, to let go. Be absolutely rigorous about not hanging on to anything.

Her dream of Dis-infection: she wanted to be drawn like a chicken—literally; her belly flapping wide open, pull out yards of entrails covered in sticky grease; she wanted to run out of herself; cut out the old sex from the sex which had been split with a knife; entrails uncoiling endlessly. I began to retch violently. Made up my mind to leave this country, this region, this room, this hiding place, this envelope. A cleaning-up job; unique; pitiless. Draining.

Is there anything left that hasn't been thrown out? No.

Begin with your near relations, no hedging; secondly, third lover, fourth mother-lover—throw up words too. Not just words: spew up languages too, cut yourself off from the past; yesterday *spricht man kein französich*; *no French spoken*. Past friendships are struck dumb, the family had breathed its last. And if he hadn't kept his word? As you deny one thing after another affirm your craving to Forget—to help you think only of him. She built up her isolation for one hundred and fifty days. She has become the spirit of negation. What absence! She still hasn't vanished. She isn't waiting, she *is* Waiting—torn apart by suffering; perhaps she is already lost in his death, already dead, in your death, lost in his corpse already, but you'll know tomorrow. You died today, you didn't know. You hear *your* news from one letter to the next: yesterday he is breathing, you are alive. Everyday, watch out for the judgement delivered in K which is not yet known to you, she is dead and she doesn't know she isn't there any more; she doesn't know she is, dead. Ah! not knowing if there is life, air, what flesh are you keeping alive in the dark? With orange juice. You are nourishing the body that is not yours any more. He is dead, perhaps, you are dead and you are still living. Ah the horror—of the bed, of the earth! where you suffer from insomnia.

What is calling you, poor body, what is lifting you up and dragging you along; what is luring you so late in the night, drawing you far away into territories where you are never ever really at home any more: lured into the crowds of

170

animate beings who know you and whom you can no longer recognize? You are invited, you go to meetings, you meet people clothed in gawdy presentness, in reality's fancy-dress. They don't attack you, reject you, greet you, see you; you are not there—(teacher should go and mind her own business)—your shadow doesn't manage to assert itself. They will wait for you, it seems; there are buildings full of halls of learning, erudite people, responsible people, reading and rubbing-out gadgets—(to make teacher's heart bleed!)—there are chairs and there is meaning, mouths to cram, languages to go over; administrations, circuses full of believers, full of sawdust and tinsel, amphitheatres full of chiefs, charges, rules, laws, provisions, permits, examinations, blindness, corridors, directions, doors through which people go in and out without howling, without collapsing thunderstruck, without bleeding ceaselessly, without falling apart, without racking their brains, without even shuddering—queues of people with whom you have no connection whatsoever. Or rather, with whom you are connected in an incomprehensible way; through incomprehension. *No entry.*

If only I had just one step to take, but it's not just a matter of taking a step, but of not putting a foot wrong, so that you can live without the outside world: not full of self-love, not self-seeking, not clinging on, but distancing yourself, not touching yourself, not looking at yourself, not hoping for anything for yourself. Ah! They don't have this sorrow—They are not scalded by joy, nor cry tears at their breasts!—You have seen the universe shuddering, through the eyes of the god of madness, you have seen the worms squirming in the cauldron.

There is a crack in the earth's surface. Such a delicate split, it's all that is left of the abyss, but it's enough. There is fire in the crack, it is taking a long time to catch, but it is drawing deeply, irrevocably; it is so slow that men have time to put it

171

out if they are afraid of it, time to extinguish it, cut if off. There is a woman who wants to travel the world inside that crack. Everyone shouts out: the fire! You are mad! But the woman allows herself to be swept away by the fire, she doesn't run away; she is not consumed by the fire, it closes in on her and doesn't bury her, as if her body were water that doesn't put it out. The face of that woman was hidden.

Today, faced with life, close to life, to death, as if you had reached the way-in, way-out, passageway, and now I am not living, I am not dead: all paths lead you astray, the nights are endless, getting longer and longer—poor sensitive, willing being —you look around at those who do not know, supremely wise, supremely naive. Strangely joyful in your sorrow. And in that joy is the strange happiness of feeling yourself close to death. Death loves me. And that gentle, agonizing love deep in your heart, is life itself.

'Do I understand you?'—Yes. What did 'understand' mean? Letter after letter, still alive, the interrogation: 'You do *know* I love you?'—Yes. Yes. Hadn't she already said yes in advance, and hadn't everything been said? She thought so. As for understanding, she would know about that later. You do know?—Yes; if you like; anything you like.

Even if she didn't know. She couldn't fail to know what was 'to be known,' inside her, between them, somewhere—*ad infinitum*—and she was moving infinitely far away from herself, till she lost sight of herself, blindly, not afraid to lose herself, in him. 'You do know how I love you'—Yes.

Listen to love's tireless inquisition: how? How? Echo him, turn it back on him; always the same insistent appeal, the words changed, the song began all over again, different words, the same tune, as if all the questions were nothing but assent's everlasting unrest, an excuse to hear the unheard of.

The music in his questions: you danced to their tune, as no

172

dancer really does; actually dancing on his body. Your soul danced to his rhythm. Your naivety. He must have thought:

'My book has been given to a woman who knows how to read and she will say: Your book is enchanting, I cannot read it.'

—Can you hear my words? Yes. You heard his words, but you couldn't hear the words within the words.

If only you had been as the shadow of a tree on the ground. But your concentration wasn't even like the shadow of a bird flitting from tree to tree, hardly the shadow of its flight.

—Whatever a love that is unique does, it's for the best, don't you think?—You believe it, without agreeing; without thinking, without saying it, you are motivated every day by that belief.

No 'I', no will: entirely in His hands. I was blameless. That was true: your 'I' was blameless, no-body was answering. Instead of being ten times more present, you were not there at all. And so far away, how could I have guessed what was to come?

The orange dress was wearing me (out). I didn't feel the ground beginning to give way under my feet.

The same question, more and more insistent, his book was being written with an implacable regularity, page by page; you thought you were reading it and that he was writing to himself. Who else but he himself could have answered the questions adequately? What were you like? A child in its mother's womb. Head between the knees. Mouth shut. His lamp shone down on my head. I was like a book that had been turned down and put aside. Eyes shut. For fear of hurting him. Don't move. Don't breathe.

Pray. I prayed. Or, more accurately, I said his name, I called him over and over again, in silence; for fear of wearying him.

173

I became his (silent) 'you.'

You asked:—Nothing will happen?—What could happen? You couldn't answer—What do you think could happen?— What are you afraid of?—How could you dare to put a name to your fear?

One day, risk asking him his own question. Suddenly feeling that it is not yours; that you have been flung into his place—And you, ah you, do I understand you?—Wretch, what have you done?—I didn't do it on purpose!—Can god be understood?—I hadn't thought of that.—The question flung me onto my own dungheap. As if the child could carry its mother in its womb!—He wasn't a god; but he was as incomprehensible as the all-consuming Presence of the divine.

—Do I understand you?—The trees tottered.—No.—If he had said yes! You would have believed him and then you would have understood him, without understanding, because he wanted you to. He would have been understood at the heart of your infinite incomprehension. How could he have said yes? And fade back into the shadows, like a book that the woman to whom it is given to read does not open.—No. You understand a great deal—Not everything?

The bird was struck down in mid-flight, its shadow lies crushed on the ground. Not even the shadow of a bird. It was the wrong question. One that answers back; and strikes where you least expect it.

—Everything? How could I? When I haven't told you everything. I have told you all I know. I have given you what I have. But there is something hidden inside me; that I don't know; that doesn't frighten me; that stays hidden. Sometimes I think that it is probably nothing but the absence of fear. None of the thoughts I have flung out in that direction has ever come close to the secret.

—Is it possible that you weren't afraid, that day?

That fear didn't touch me. I wasn't there. Even if everything was happening inside your body, when it was taking place you were not there to notice it. You were beyond letters and beyond questions, far away from the house where you waited for them, received them, dreaded them. They came at you, from him, their black wings spread out in the desert to nourish your body.

—Look for me. I want you to go looking for me as I am looking for you.
—How?
—As if you had not been found yet, when you thought everything had been given in advance, as if you had never been found. Because, if I had found you, if I didn't have to search for you, fighting from hour to hour against all the obstacles within me and outside me, within you and around you, between you and me—I would be quite different, I would be god then. Humbly, you longed for the opposite, a longing to be put aside, suppressed: 'Find me! Please let him find me.' Your amazement at the horror of a meeting that didn't take place, that did and didn't happen. He was calling himself, from so far away, and was searching for me, so insistently, because of the distance: to keep me at a distance; to protect you; to protect himself.
—But look within us. So as not to be god.
—I long for you. He could say that sentence in ten different ways and you veered from happiness to unhappiness, from humility to pride. Sometimes it was life, sometimes shit—ecstasy overturned.

The tormenting tenderness in his imperious commands; the same old appeal yet different, more and more urgent, each day a little more pressing; wavering between uncertainty and trust, then something else crept in between two words—and everything had to be considered in a new light.

Back and forth went his critical inquisition, without a

break. Gently he hacked away at your silence. Such a finely honed knife that could cut your throat without breaking the skin. As if he had tested the cutting edge on his fingers and tongue. I didn't even feel it plunging in, back and forth, no need of force. Painlessly, I was penetrated, answers followed from the inquisition, in silence and blood.

Were you deaf? He wrote to you: 'I have always been afraid of being in the position of the traveller who returns home and exclaims: I'm back: why isn't there anyone here? And he hears himself saying: I wrote; why didn't anyone reply? He hears his voice trembling with anger and is humiliated, since anger is hateful to him. And what is more, it is ridiculous precisely because there is no one there to answer for it. What is absolutely unbearable is seeing oneself transformed into living wrath: I have come, I was full of love and joy. And here I am forced to be mean and aggrieved. Why should he be ashamed and loathe himself? For whom? For no-one. But he has no alternative, because he has gone so deeply inside love. Into the dangerous shared space. Why do you think I have this fear from time to time?'

I heard him. I would have been hard put to reply by return of post. But I didn't feel I had to. Didn't our mutual understanding take care of everything in advance? It wasn't a disturbing fear; only a phantom from another time. I had my ghosts too. Why should I listen to them? When I already had so much trouble disentangling the ten tones of his voice, which gave every one of his sentences ten different meanings. And so much trouble grasping each message above the uproar caused by anguish, and the rumbling of the iron lung? One single breath from his chest answered all my questions and dispelled my darkness. I asked for nothing more.

In harmony, like a child in the womb, everything is understood in silence. I was loved in advance. Deaf and dumb because I trusted.

176

*

—Were you blind?

No. There were screens between the letters and what I read. Window-panes. Because of the distance and the signs of the struggle. There were things in between. Sometimes you looked at him through nine panes, other times one single curtain separated you, and you could pull it aside. He kept nothing from you, that you couldn't doubt. He spoke openly.

'You see how I look at you? Look at me as I am looking at you. Read my letters without hiding: and you will see clearly what I am doing for us.'

I drew the veil aside, opened the window, created space and silence around me, so that I could get close to the page. I washed my hands, wiped my face, I even dried love's tears to read him more closely; I tried to guess his state of health by the length of his letter; to see whether he was trying his strength. He gave you his naked book to read; it is that nakedness that makes you say: I cannot read you without hiding behind a little silence.

The unrelenting patience of his future tenses: 'You will tell me about yourself.' 'Yes.' A patience you couldn't get round. You will talk to me about yourself; not about me. As I am telling you about myself. The silence would be broken. You didn't want to think about the day you would talk to him, you hardly wanted to hope for it, however faint and apprehensive the hope might be.

'You said: yes. Now don't let your "yes" be caught unprepared. I'll be back. Listen to me: you must be at least ten times "you" when I come home to you. I know you can say to me: come back first, then I'll answer you. I have told you: I am coming back. Meet me half-way. Tell me if something is holding you back. Come. I shall love you as I love you now, as I have never loved you. I love you already as never before. Because you haven't said no.'

A patience capable of holding out till the end. Till you are exhausted.—Do you think I am asking too much of you?—No. No.—I am only asking for what I would like to give you. I am calling for your sake.

His wish to bring you to yourself.—This evening look at yourself through my eyes. Write me what you see. You will look at yourself. You were looking at yourself. Through nine misty glass panes.—Am I asking for the impossible? If so, give it to me.—Drag yourself step by step to meet his wishes; I was crawling along. To give him the impossible. If it hurts you, be glad. A harsh love—corresponding to my future joy.

You will give me. Impossible to give; not to give.

Go part of the way, not half-way, just a little part of the first turning—what is stopping you from writing to him? How could I explain the inexplicable? It couldn't be written. You couldn't do the impossible.

Neither the strength, nor the words. Limbs paralysed. The body wouldn't get up, the mind wouldn't spark; the heart was beating but the eyes were blind—I wasn't in touch with my flesh.

Not *the* impossible: what is impossible for *you*. I had come face to face with my body and I couldn't find myself in it.

—One day I don't know when, in ten days or ten months, you will be able to. It was inconceivable. But you could conceive of it.

—I will wait. You do want my wait to be your wait, don't you? Answer me. I shall be waiting so impatiently for your answer! Please answer me, won't you? I am so impatient for your answer, tell me if you are waiting as I am. I am so anxious for your answer. Don't you want me to have it too?

Answer. Answer. Answer. Answer. That is his wish, that is your wish. What is stopping you? The stuff I'm made of.

You hadn't the strength to resist—and he knew it.

—You must answer me. Therefore you will. And if you want to please me even more, you will send a telegram the moment you have decided to answer. Because I am waiting confidently but I am in torment.

I was confronting my body. I was being besieged by a great
king. He was raising powerful redoubts around me. The city
wanted to be taken. But there was no one to be found inside
the city to deliver it up. Despite appeals, gentle threats. I
dreaded opening the letters. I couldn't see how I could avoid
answering any more. But I didn't have the answer. No
strength for an answer, let alone the strength to give one.

His brutal, passionate patience. 'When you answer me I will
come. I will be with you straightaway.'

Who is this foreign king inside your body? Who is stopping
you going forwards?—No one that I know of. Did a passer-by
get in?—Open your mouth and speak. I longed to speak.

   —Open your eyes and go in—I was so afraid I wouldn't be
able to say the thing he was waiting for; afraid of approaching
the thing; which repelled me. I was standing in front of the
body, back against the door, hoping for divine aid to set me
free. What I longed to do didn't take place. A strange silence
holds my tongue. In front of the mirror, tortured, this battle is
ridiculous—Caress yourself as if you were me. Turn your
hands into mine. Open yourself as if you were opening my last
letter.

My hands on my body, heavy as stone.

Letter on top of letter. The envelopes in my hands; open the
envelope with your eyes shut. Blue paper. Black letters.
Terrified me.
   —It doesn't matter if you don't answer. I shouldn't have
asked. The miracle is probably impossible. Let's not think
about it any more. Pretend I didn't say anything. Blame my
insistence on the love I am wanting to give you. Don't worry
about it. I have faced you with the possible and the

179

impossible. So you can see yourself; avoid seeing yourself, as I see you.

To be cursed and blessed in the same breath—of his desire.

I was in front of the mirror. Everything is in the hands of love. Except my courage.

—Just make the first move. Open your legs. Pretend he is there. Pretend his hands are caressing you, his palms on your thighs, his holy spirit breathing on your pubis, his blessing hands on your hips; your sex is in the hands of heaven; pretend god is coming to you through your thick fuzz—but then this path brings you face to face with your life.

I was starting. In the mirror, hands easily between my thighs—it was turning out to be an easy path.

A woman was sitting at a cross-roads. In front of her two paths opened out, went off, vanished; were lying in wait for her; forbade her to move; to choose life, death. I put myself entirely in my own hands.

My hips in the mirror spreading endlessly; the pubis rising like a high mountain; my own lands terrified me; how could I subdue such formidable flesh? My weary, timid fingers. His letter is in my willing hands. Between two tracks, view obstructed, division. It was a bit too dark in the mirror. No strength to open the envelope. To read the sensual lines with my own eyes. All my desire is in my hands and I can't lift a finger. The path had plunged into thorns. Passions unleashed against passions. If you can't bring yourself to life, or to death, take yourself by storm. I attacked. I took one, two steps. Such a narrow path. No one can follow you. Your body was unwilling to let you in. If you don't want to go in, go in anyway. All my limbs and almost all my organs obeyed. If you go in, despite yourself, no eye will see you. You shouldn't say: I can't turn myself on. I can't possibly commit incest. Actually that's just what you can do. No, no. If you besiege the city despite yourself, your eyes will be of no use any more. Your sight will be taken away. Your hands will be cut off from you. My hands moved forward into the foreign flesh, of my

180

sex. My fingers had decided to conquer it. The envelope was thick, I had trouble breaking it open, I inserted my index finger with difficulty, the edges were stuck together, the paper turned hard and horny. If you read this letter the sun will stop in its course. Let your hands go into a place where no-body knows them. I got into the city despite my disgust, no-body recognized me and I couldn't see any-body. How can I find my bearings there? No-body to ask. Surrounded by walls. I groped my way. When I opened the letter my eyes closed, no eye read to me what the cunt desires. Silence reigns. The flesh remained a dead letter. My hands returned to impotence and ashes.

His grey letter.—Don't be sad. Think about it. It doesn't matter your hands didn't succeed. I kiss your hands that didn't get what I wanted. You should have told me about the king. Never mind about me, I'll get over it. You obviously can't open yourself to me completely. My heart is heavy; it'll pass. If you can, think about it, do—for yourself.

Grey on sepia, his epistles, I was in the hands of heaven and the heavens were overcast, the letters were clouding the heavens; I was dragging myself along the path not knowing if it would end. Crawling slowly forwards, thirty years, another hundred to go; you were dying to rest, to die. Alone. No support. No reason. No hope.

—My hope that you will come has no solid basis. That's why there is hope. Tell me about the king.

Helpless. My longing to do what is terrifying. Do it for yourself: for no-body. For love of he who is: all; who is incomprehensible—to you. My sex terrified me.

—*Tell me about the king.*—What king?—The one inside you? Think. You let a passer-by in, next he's a lover, finally he is king of the castle.

—When I come, let me be coming home. Tell me about the stranger now.—What stranger? I searched for him, thought about him, went through the rooms of the castle, terrified, hoping to find someone there, whom I would recognize; hoping to start in terror. To attack him instantly, to do battle with him. To throw him out. To kill him. To drag away his corpse. To bury him in a foreign land and forget him under the stones.

—Don't make me feel I am coming home to be knifed; stabbed in the chest when I reach my room. See to it that I can rest easy.

I tried and tried. And what if you don't succeed? Love will see to it. I really couldn't see any one. Nothing but the clouded mirror and memory's bottomless pit merging into the night.

—If you want to keep me alive, don't let any one be waiting for your husband with a knife. Do more than you need. At the very last minute there will still be time . . .

I wasn't deaf. But I had trouble hearing everything he didn't say. There were silences I didn't know how to translate; letters remained unread; I opened them, they remained closed to me; dreams couldn't be interpreted. 'Let's hurry, let's make an end to all this. I don't want to be tortured any longer by the thought that life will begin without you ever having answered me beforehand.' If I had been able to read that letter, I would have trembled with shame. But something prevented it from reaching me. Did it arrive? Yes. It was grey, I opened it, shuddering, I read it differently. He was alive. 'I am alive,' it told me, the rest was wiped out. Read without reading—there's no contradiction.

There is a city; its inhabitants are invisible.

The sepia letters:—You can't see them, then? Do I have to describe them to you myself? Must I introduce them to you?

Its gloomy streets broke off: dead-ends; ramparts round the outside—impossible to penetrate. I shrank from touching the ground; I was running on tip-toe.

182

—Tell me about your ghosts. Who haven't you thought about since we were born?

No one, no one.—No ghosts?—Not that I know of.—Not a soul: a woman? You say there is no king but you don't say anything about a woman stranger.

Tell me about her.—Never a woman, never.—Don't tell me it's impossible. Admit it is possible. Otherwise I shall be alarmed.

It was an impossible possibility. I'd never thought of it.

—You haven't dreamt of her? Met her? Run away from her? Hidden her?

If that is not the truth my memory's at fault: my necropolis. On all fours, among the tombs, horrified, I tried to read the inscriptions, unfortunately the names had been erased, fortunately, as soon as I approached, bent my face nearer it was caught by the stone, no sooner did a letter flicker than it died away. That letter didn't remind me of anyone.

His blue pants:—My love, wear them for me, until I take them back. *But—beware—if you do—wear them feeling woman's love.*

Put them on tonight. And if you dream: know yourself.

Three letters and three telegrams to avoid telling the dream that beat me, overcame me and reduced me to anguish. As if I had had intercourse with a beast. As if you were a beast. Unwitting. I had nothing to do with it personally. It happened brutally. Fate paved the way. It was a question of going straight to the climax. But you weren't even thinking about it. I was in the foreign city. Absolutely separate. It wasn't my dream. There were no moral laws, ties, conventions. I had no mother, no daughter, no self, no importance. It was the king's dream. Things had a simplicity I never would have thought of. Split, I went straight to myself, to my fate: straight to the king; I didn't care who he was, that he had his time and I had mine; what did I care about public opinion, affection, whether I knew him or not? I went further and further away from myself.

Do you hate your father, mother, children, your own life?

183

Neither hate nor love. The king made the first move. And you went out of yourself.

It didn't matter who he was: the point was his height, his strong legs, his prophetic stature, the force of his desire. You were dashing along the streets for one reason only. Neither love nor hate—flesh makes fate. All the rest is irrelevant. Straight out of yourself to the king.

Wearing black, you have to enter a place where no one knows anyone. And do what you desire—But don't profane the divine pants—Not what I desire. What desire decides.

The king has come only for you. No comment. Heat was rising up from the street—it was a simple straightforward affair, that had been brewing for ages, it was already agreed, only the idea was missing. The blood was humming through your veins, the king was nothing to me, desire was in charge. You are not being asked for your love.

You have to go through life straight to the point. And do what the king desires. Instead of love, understanding—the other splendour. Go from desire straight to desire. Pass through the first room without flinching, then the second room without letting yourself be stopped. With no memory. But keep your soul apart. Separate your story from sexuality. Go where no one is watching anyone. Blindly, helplessly, without interpreting. Without indulgence. No explanations. Desire will take care of the last move. On all fours then, crawl between the tables of the law, as if they had been reduced to their simplest expression: Come. Get on with it. My clothes were undone. The last room was not far off, my gown was floating loose, the king was stark naked, no face, no names, the sex was enough, things took over, you were naked before you knew it, the king has only come to be beside (your) no-body. He had dreamt of no one but you. Copulation took place involuntarily. I didn't even know who it was. As for me, I got up in the night and went through the rooms of our life. As I was alone a man wrestled with me till day-break. And when he saw he couldn't master me, he touched me in the hollow of the groin. And I said: let me go, and he said: I am doing what you desire, and I said to him: what is your name? and he replied: what does my name matter, I am he whom you desire. He touched you between the thighs and you came as if it were really Him. He was far too close for me to see his face.

It was a strange dream. Why not tell it? Why not?

—Tell me the king's true name.—What king? What name? I couldn't see his face. It wasn't me dreaming.—No letter tomorrow, don't be angry with me, I can't write to the king's home. How long? *How long*? Don't you want all this to end? You are forcing me to torment us! Your dreams stop me sleeping. I love you so much that I'll do all I can to write tomorrow. You see how you split me.

And I couldn't even die of shame, nor even call the thing that was destroying my voice unhappiness.

The letter with no beginning, no invocation, no name, no signature. The letter of Resignation. A scrap of paper. Torn from my letter of Omission.

'I have just read your letter. What a pity. I think I should come very soon. When do you think I could? When will you stop putting me off? Giving me the feeling that you are drawing back? Holding me at a distance from myself when you should be bringing me closer? Do you think I should come?. Do you think I am being deceived? Tell me what you think about it? Because I trust you more than anyone. Don't I? You see how much I love you?' No signature. No room. I am stunned. Distraught. In danger of screaming. The only possible good that can come of love's agony is its power to wipe out all other suffering instantly. But there isn't any good. And anyway, I didn't think that. I couldn't hope to die and I couldn't hope to live through another moment like that.

The tiny blue letter: 'I am here, my love. Don't panic.

Yesterday's letter isn't from me. Your letter dictated it. I couldn't sign it.'

Between the two letters, heart failure, black mist in front of the eyes, you are swallowed up by the darkness, death deep down in the breast, nothingness seeping into your lungs.

Yesterday, all is lost. All can still be saved. Never mind about what's missing. A day or two after your death you were hauled out of the muddy pit, dragged to the bed by ropes and put back on your feet, as if you had been carried away by a bad dream.

'*Wait till you get the wedding letter.*' Soon the letter of Compensation. Watch out for it from one day to the next. When? Soon. 'I have made my decision.'—'Do you think I am hurting you? Try and find a time when it's neither night nor day, that's when I'll stop loving you.'

Sometimes life, sometimes the abyss. 'That you have kept us apart won't stop you coming. It would be better not to wait any longer. How happy I shall be the day I call you! If you love me the way I love you, pretend it's tomorrow. Let's not wait any longer!'

Every day is the last day before the day of the Summons. 'Just let me prepare myself for our joy, then I will say to you: Come. *Will you be surprised!*' His words: a hammer smashing up a rock—striking sparks from it. His passion was trifling with me.

—Were you afraid? yes, no. Fear wasn't the word. It was worse. But it passed. A death had occurred—brutally. Nothingness had surged up. There was nothing left. Nothing? Almost nothing. The remains of a scaffold.

—Pretend nothing happened. Willingly. I did. I escaped the scaffold!

And yet I remember that it seemed inescapable.

Page after page, get over the letters leading up to the summons. Even if the envelope was sepia? If he wrote in pencil? in black ink? Signs have meaning. But signs are not infallible. No one in my dreams any more. No one I knew. No

186

one living. A dead man wrestled with me till day-break, and he didn't touch me. I looked the dead man in the face. And I didn't die.

Dream after dream without a word. Without a name. The catastrophe didn't take place.

—Nothing can happen to me. What is vulnerable is not me.

What happened next? The events you can never talk about, even to yourself. And yet they went right through your body. But they are never happening to you. I see them taking place over there, a little further north. In the third room by the door: between the breasts (on the fortieth street). I have already told this story to several people and to one person, to someone else too, to a close relative and to a distant one, in the hope that telling it would bring it back to me. In the hope that his letter would reach me. I would touch the paper. I would know. It would come to an end. The past could begin.

If you don't get the letter it's because you don't have an address. This story will not be read. If it were written down no one could read it. Believe it. It contains scandalous letters. Why don't you write it? It would never be read.

And today I remember that for a long time he called me *Shorthair*. I had very short hair. Shorter and shorter. But this name no longer appeared in the last letters. At that time, just before the summons, he told me that he had grown a beard, because of the hospital and I thought about his other face; unexpected. You will see me. The one I had never seen before. For the first time.

Then the last message but one: '*Next time ours*,' so, the next letter I'd be off, I was ready to leave, suspense shattered; there was still some waiting left, some to-ing and fro-ing, but then

187

the departure, the first—the end of our waiting. The letter would certainly come, you couldn't doubt it. *Next time.* Next time, The Time. And then the final call, *jetzt*, the same day, by the same post, the two letters at once, as if the call were calling itself; listening to itself and re-calling itself; to celebrate itself; in two different languages; and in all the other languages, all calling me once and for all time—*jetzt*, now, *Come*—as if it were telling me to come and start life in eternity. And *jetzt* was the name for our eternity; the name to bring me to him. His confident writing on strips of shiny paper torn from a single page. And there had been nothing before this. I would set out, I would arrive, and it would be eternity. Did you believe it? I couldn't believe it, I couldn't disbelieve it. I was going. *Jetzt*. Instantly. All I had to do was catch the plane; to live in eternity. The call had reached me. I had received the letter. The god of madness was awaiting me. He hasn't written to anyone else. And no one could have come after me.

No one to whom I could tell what happened next: the things in this story that could never be written down. There is something that cannot be told. Not here, in the time of this world. Something that can only be written down when my languages are worn out, in infinity, where the god of life, of death, would be talking to himself in his own language. It is a question of an end without an ending. A death that is not over, that I am still savouring today. In strict privacy. It is a question of loving to distraction, a love that renders language powerless. A question of the unique, inhuman love that the god of madness had for me. And no one would understand it. It was a terrifying love that arrested life and blunted death's power.

The frightful love that god holds against you and that forces you to be loved by him—to (his) distraction.

Come, now, where I love you beyond yourself, as no one else ever has, where I love you more than yourself, for love of you, and I shall make love to you—differently. And you will beg in anguish: 'Don't do that, don't love me more, if you loved me any more, I would go out of my mind.'

You need the unique language, you don't have it, the language that speaks to you alone, the one that spoke to me; he told me things that no one but him can understand; and no one but mad-me could have heard him calling me by my name, except the self that I cannot be, here. You need the special language. To relate what is unrelated. To tell of the things that happened there, where life halts between love and the god who says each thing for the last time, the language that I can no longer speak here. I haven't got it, but I can hear it still, once and for all time.

The sun stopped in its course.

You would need writing to open its mouth and cry out, paper to writhe, shrink, fall on its knees, fold up; paper that can't hear itself screaming, that holds back suffering and contains the pain, for love of the mad god. But you write through clenched teeth, from the death which escapes you: I spoke that language when I was alone in the regions you can only reach Afterwards.

With no precedent, no purpose, no consequence, no resistance.

He came only to be with me. I went, I came back, I kept quiet. I went far beyond myself, beyond love itself, till I reached the Present. *Jetzt.* Now: in his language the name for time began with his initial. He had written it in a firm marriage hand. In red ink; in one sitting. The letters were joined forever. It was the end of a year. Just before eternity. *Next time yours.*

The first plane, for love of the man in whose womb you wanted to dream just once. You didn't want to be parted from him any more than the blood in his own breast. You wanted to be him, to cease to be myself just once, to avoid feeling the vast gap that separated me from him, while I was getting as close as any human being could, to his body, his real skin; you wanted to stop suffering each time my lips touched his, suffering because I was not in him, not inside his flesh, not coming and going ceaselessly in his heart. Because it is only there, deep inside, that the pain could cease.

Ten years to wring from my body the strength to take the next step. You could have told madness: 'You are my sister.' You call hate 'my love.' And death your true mother.

It was the time of the Great Loneliness. I was outside. You can only get there on your own. No ordinary language was spoken; nothing can be explained. The things that happened were not expressed in words; I knew them; I carried them out. They were decided in our bodies. I saw everything. From the point of view of eternity. Everything was crucial. Decisions were made in our flesh, without a word.

When everything is at a distance, speech returns, you could speak; but these things can't be told, no human voice can make them understood. They can only take place over there in Solitude.

It all happened in the Absolute. You can only get to the Absolute when you are out of your mind. After you have forgotten everything. Lost everything: normal life, sight. Goods. Possessions. Bodies. When you are not holding onto anything any more. You don't get there from here; you don't start from a land; a ground; a city; a desire. It isn't decided here. You have been called. You don't ask yourself where, how, who. When the call came I answered it. You can only get there by doing violence to yourself.

You can't possibly go if you are not freed from here. You have to have paid the entrance fee 'up there'. How much? Everything. Cut off everything. Burn everything that is left.

190

Cut yourself off absolutely. Become alien. Feel the other's powerful presence inside you, stronger than you, and cease to be anyone but the other. If you haven't kept anything of yourself, nothing can prevent you from reaching the Absolute, no chance of coming back. Then you love to distraction, giddy with terror. And that terror is your greatest joy. For you are now the other.

I had paid. Wiped out my past. Killed. Lost. All ties had been cut, with knife, soul, teeth—every one of the human languages cut off. I didn't speak mine any more. I listened to the other language, I heard it at a distance. I knew it was being spoken for me alone. I didn't know the language, I accepted it. It announced. Questioned. I answered with my blood. It reached me, touched me. I gave in to it wherever it lead me. Without stopping myself. All the time. Every moment leaping into the infinite. And what anguish every moment; leaping, falling, what an effort, failing, what an ambition, I shall never manage to answer fast enough, fly high enough—and that short-coming proved: my suffering and my compensation.

If I hadn't devoted all my energies to renouncing everything every moment, forgetting each being and each thing throughout the whole wide world in order to cut myself off from time; if I hadn't got rid of myself, of every last wish, even the tiniest thought, the plane in which I was flying to him in silence could never have taken off. If I had made as if to turn round, to look overboard, it could not have passed into the infinite. It would have crashed.

It was the first of January. It had been as hard for me to reach the Absolute as it had been for Tantris not to die, despite the waiting. Nine days to weigh anchor, nine days for the crossing, nine days within sight of the shore unable to land, because of the storm—and each day was much longer than nine days. Losing faith and regaining it depending on the wind, depending on my anguish; perishing nine times, however much I longed to get there; the sky torn by angry waves had turned into the sea; emerging nine times from the depths only to be hurled back down—from abyss to abyss—in the end you fell from the skies, unexpectedly, the sea was calm, you landed in the shadows where the earth let you—beside myself with terror, but filled with an inexplicable joy.

The hotel was enchanted. I leant on the desk, tried to give his name. Perhaps I should only have given one of them. But which one? Names crowded in, none seemed to me to be real or powerful enough. He had called himself Tantris in his last telegram. I didn't know his real name.

'Come. We will have everything. And I will tell you my name.' It was the first test: shouldn't I have guessed in what name god was awaiting me? All you have done for him will be worthless if in this big moment you don't help yourself against death.

I murmured all the names he might have had in books, and the names that he was hidden behind in finite languages. And what if it were forbidden by law? The names left the law unmoved. The hall was vast and empty. The hotel had been evacuated the day before. God's names aroused no response. As if he were not known. The law wasn't malicious. Go and look for him, if you wish. Explore the enchanted, deserted hotel. The place which had been crowded with people was now silent. A huge museum of words with no echo. All life arrested. I explored with the eyes of memory. Everything in retrospect: I saw myself wandering before through its deserted rooms, searching from bottom to top for the room that had been reserved; going back down the halls till I came to the day before; I saw the inhabitants who were still alive then, moving away from me. I met mummified men and women throughout the long galleries: how young you look, what's your secret, actually we stopped growing ten years ago. I had roamed round here before, ten years ago; looking for my life: for him. Under the stern but indulgent eyes of the law. The number of names that came back to me in vain.

How could you fail to get lost? Where is he-whom-you-are-seeking? In all the places you expect to find him. Go in and out through several doors at once, suffering, split yourself up so you can lie in wait for him everywhere at once, among crowds of beings you have met before, forgotten, without recognizing anyone, no time, not in the mood—I am searching for my Sorrowful one, he whose name escapes me.

When you have given up hope, when you have been all over the place in vain, inside and outside, even into what has been repressed, into old texts and the most recent books, without finding him; if you see yourself pacing through time as if you were seeking someone who had called you in an irresistible language, a language you didn't know very well but which knew you perfectly; if you hear yourself calling him by all the names that might reach him, please him, be worthy of him, and you don't get an answer—gradually you don't dare shout any more, you scarcely dare murmur; gradually you slow down, don't run any more, you stop because you have to begin thinking that there is no sign because he is nowhere where you can meet him. You have to think this in order to prevent yourself from thinking that he certainly would have answered; if he had existed. You are going to wake up at the end of the gallery; better not move; better stay quiet. If the curtain of mist on which you were projecting your desires finally cleared it would reveal the blank wall of your future. When you have made quite sure that there isn't the smallest crack in the house that could give you what you are seeking, and not the slightest chance of ever coming through, you know without a doubt that you will never make the journey, never see the only face that saddens you—I have been sent out into the light never to see him again—you arrive quite painlessly at that old comfort: death—all is lost, nothing is lost, there is no reason to go on struggling and you lie down at last in the last bed, face turned to the wall, you won't get Life's Letter. It is at that moment, just when you have lain down, that there's a violent knocking at the door—and so I haven't the right to withdraw in peace? You are wanted on the phone, you are being asked to answer, 'You should have gone through customs,' 'I have nothing left to declare,' you go out on to the stairs, painfully, 'it's for the last farewell'— Anguish—weariness! The bed moves away. And so you are not allowed to die when you are still living? Worn out, you go down among a familiar crowd. Fight your way to the phone—and it is his voice! In one leap you are outside the funereal tribe, higher up, further away, in bright sunlight. As if your last burst of weariness had swept you away to the other world, the one on the other side of the wall: what could not happen to you is happening, what was refused has been granted, with the same inexorable simplicity. You would not be able to escape. Yesterday: you will not go. Here: you will. It is the same power as before, operating by decree, but everything which was forbidden before is now ordained. You will see him. The future had already begun.

So, the absolute had always been there, beside you, but you couldn't see it. All you had to do was to stop waiting. Give up. Turn your face to the wall. Then you would be free to see that you had been on board from the start. They were only waiting for your soul to weigh anchor.

It was a deceptive January. The man I had given up was already there. He was leaning over you. His face mutilated from the last battle. I didn't dare take it in. If he has lost an eye isn't it to acquit you? That is certainly the price that the Fatal Illness demanded of him. He has been made to pay for your imperfection: the way you lost sight of him: didn't recognize him. But it was his smile. His teeth lighting my darkness. He promised me thirteen days and thirteen nights. To explore the countryside with no limits. He with whom you never thought you would journey. Already up there, already in the cabin that he had chosen. Thirteen years per day, and thirteen years per night. With him. He has changed. That doesn't stop him being eternal.

Thirteen lifetimes with him. For certain. These things happen when you don't believe in them. You can move. It's not a dream. It will be exceptionally fine. Once—again.

Woman's dream is to be feared, every woman should beware. I was not dreaming. The more passionately a woman has longed to find herself, the more irrevocably will she lose herself in a dream. Alas! It wasn't a dream.

Today still, after five thousand years, it is as hard for me to tell the truth without being struck dumb as it is for me to give up wanting to tell the truth over and over again. As if it wasn't true.—Who can beat life to death?—If you are capable of renouncing this desire you can tell the real truth, the truth that stopped being true the moment I tried to picture it.

I didn't beat life to death. Life wanted to die.

Here it is: I approached him. I had arrived and it was true.

The room was small and dingy, so narrow that there was little more than a step between the bed and the door. No window; I could hardly make out the shapes in the darkness. It was a real hotel room.

I opened the door, went in, approached him. I forgot fear, death, the outside, the past, the storm, the future; I forgot my history, my origin, my name. My life vanished. I must have closed the door behind me. I had nothing more to be. I was one step away from god. If that.

There is one step that no one can talk about. There is one scene that writing cannot handle in writing. You can write everything, in all languages, all books are written to avoid writing the thing. I am so close to it. I could put my finger on it. It is in the room. Everything is there: bed, chair, telephone, a rose, the time of times, you yourself body and soul, and

195

god as he has always been. You see him, you see everything, nothing is hidden. There are all the words you need. It can't be written. It's not I who am failing. I have done the necessary a thousand times. I have made all the first moves. I have tackled the scene every day for ten years, my body is worn out from reliving it. But everything has always halted in front of the bed, as if writing were ashamed of its weakness. I would need another kind of writing to follow me, capable of understanding what happened in the room without going mad too.

While you were worrying, travelling, wandering around resigned, your relations with him were more painful but they were less incomprehensible.

Everything was gratuitous: anguish, absence, journey, multiple wounds. Everything had been paid for in advance. I cried out. And he re-turned the knife of his silence in my wound.

If you wished to talk with your god, not once in a thousand years would he answer you in your language. That's why I had wanted to talk with him.

So that I could question him, call him a thousand times with no fear of being betrayed, of being deceived. I wanted to write him a thousand letters to get the thousand silences I deserved. Send him a telegram: 'Reassure me, please. I am alone.' Why ask him to do that if it were true? His answer was in my prayers: they were not prayers, but his silence that was piercing me. Besides, it wasn't his silence exactly but my babbling, trying to make his name sound. That is why I was begging him; sent him a cable, signed 'Your,'—His answer didn't come; it was there. My voice met his silence. What took place between my heart, lungs and throat I shall never understand. The voice that I could hear saying: 'Alone, alone, I am your,' wasn't really mine. I knew beforehand that

196

he understood everything I would say. I was alone with my loneliness. So I wasn't really alone: I was protected by him. My loneliness understood me; his silence: the very voice of the one with whom I wished to talk. I was alone. I was with him.

If he had answered my call, I wouldn't have believed he was giving me an answer. He didn't have to. If he had said to me: 'I am listening.' I wouldn't have had anything to ask. I trusted his silence, it hurt me to trust it. I was being tortured by love, I sensed that love was carrying me away, far from my possibilities, I offered no resistance, as if I were turning into another whose love went beyond me. The movement of that love was paradoxical: it proved that it was a question of god, he who separates absolutely. But that was not inexplicable.

If he passed right by me I wouldn't see him. Knowing that reassured me. There was no chance of missing him.

Perfect Solitude.

I was standing in front of the bed. Outside space. The hotel hadn't really changed, but it hardly existed. The room was receding. I was one step away from god, at last. I knew it was the first. Ten thousand years ago; yesterday. He had just said to me 'You see . . .' I wanted to interrupt him. I could see him. I wanted to have just arrived, I wanted to go back, come to the door again, put my case down in the dark, the world vanished, perhaps I didn't knock, I'll never be in front of this door again, the door that could no longer separate, I could not see him yet, never looked at before, I knew I was going to see him, it would be the first time, it was absolutely certain, he was lying in the room: nothing would tear him away from me, on fire with passion, the blood pounding in my head, I didn't hear his voice very well, he must have said *Come in*, and in his tone was the laughter of eternity. He was there, he would be there, I had heard him say 'You see . . .' and everything was really true. So intensely real and true that it was beyond me, I

197

couldn't manage to go on exactly where I was, there was a gap between belief and me, I was standing in front of him, face to face, my belief astonished, it was too true for me to take it in. And yet he was talking to me, me, me—and I was so sure, so unsure of being saved. At first in a language in which 'thou' doesn't exist. Then in a language in which 'thou' is said.

'*Siehst du* . . .' Yes! I said to interrupt, in order to hear once again, and for the first time, and for all the others, his voice which was too serious, the pressure of his voice, the calm, the space, the pressure of each letter to be graven in the flesh of eternity. I was standing before the eternal. I had heard him say to me 'You see' time could stop. The sentence was going on . . .

I had just shut the door. I had just stopped. Desiring. Fearing. As if nothing could happen any more. I had just opened the door ten years ago. I was going to take the last step. It would be the first. No more doubt. The bed wasn't a fiction. The first sentence ended. It only reached me later.

'You see. I am alive . . .' I saw. He was alive. His voice was announcing it. 'I have come back from the dead.' I must have been overcome with joy. I accepted the sentence, it went in, I remember its inflection, I was deep inside the room, the sentence penetrated and settled in my depths. At that moment I was too close to god to understand it. I didn't have the strength to look at him enough. Too much of him and not enough of me. I couldn't get over being there.

When god, the one who nearly died, is finally before you, every word comes towards you from the back of the room with a hidden violence.

He had just flung a sentence at me. Suddenly everything was suspended. I had an impulse to flee. My head was empty. A sentence was approaching whose sense would only reach me at the last minute. In the end I would understand it, too late. For the moment it was only on its way, it hadn't touched me. There was a little warning. I knew I would get it; recognize it with terror. As soon as I shut the door my heart started beating, my pulse racing, a silence in my throat, I dropped into the room as silence drops into silence. Blood was dripping from the ceiling, I was fascinated with terror. At least that was my delusion. I had spotted the stain. When god, the one you love, is lying down in front of you, in reality, who is stopping you moving forward, who is crushing you, carrying you away? No window-pane, no glass, no trace of the past, all I had to do was touch him. The thoughts must have rushed out of my head. The sentence was rumbling towards me word after word. It was as if I had suddenly found myself in a strange hotel room where, from one moment to the next, time was slowing down, dragging on and on, falling over itself according to its crazy laws and things reached me one by one: from different sides, words from different times in which I wasn't living. I had entered the last room, I didn't remember when, and I found myself somewhere else. The sentence was going to go off, it was a blazing canon ball, its fuse was burning down, it rolled on alone, propelled from the mouth I worshipped. I was transfixed by his smile; drawn by it; paralysed by it. I hurled myself to the left to avoid it—in vain. I would have had to overcome a fatal slowness, I had become, in front of him, passivity itself. I had become that formless space out of which I had to wrench each infinitely feeble impulse to think—an exhausting effort—in order to drag one single step forwards out of that nothingness. The door was quite near me, but somewhere else, and I couldn't reach it. Because I wasn't separated from it by space but by centuries of another time. I was trying to tear my voice free from terror, trying to shift the vast expanse of stagnant water. As if *the* distance between Him and what I was didn't exist—the distance I would never get over. I must have lost all hope already. To save myself I would have had to put space between the sentence and me, to protect me from the explosion and the shrapnel's deadly blast. I was caught,

199

paralysed, my will had to fight its way up from the depths of a body which did not obey me, I couldn't even moan in my death agony; I couldn't haul myself out of the floods of molten metal. My body was keeping me down; I couldn't even get to the head of the bed, which I wouldn't reach anyway until I was exhausted. I had such a passionate longing to understand the sentence without understanding it, to twist its meaning, to go on living afterwards—but this longing was buried so far down—and I couldn't have cried out my sentence: '*I* am alive'—the words were buried. I was alone, not far from the bed, caught in the immense crystal of loneliness and I wouldn't survive.

The room was going to explode in his face, the face god set against me. With a horribly painful movement I struggled desperately to move away; to swim ten years through the stony waves, to reach the head of the bed. I don't know how I got two yards from the door, quite close to him, my strength shattered.

You wake up in the middle of the night, to escape the sentences that had been haunting you—clinging like caterpillars—your mouth, throat, lungs full of hair—you wake in another body ready to give up everything—your body is paralysed with terror, but because I could see him I was fascinated—it wouldn't be long before the sentence went off. I would have liked him to say a different one to me. I had left everything outside, the past was passed, I couldn't go in, with no possessions, no peace, no name, it wouldn't have changed anything even if I had brought them along. I would have liked to hear a sentence with room for me in it. But he had spoken to me from *his* triumph. I needed all the strength of my love to watch him saying to me: 'I am alive,' as if *I* were death. I fought my way through the stony waters. My paralysis infected the world, the sentence stopped too, the bomb had not gone off, really god alone knew when the explosion would take place.

That first sentence went on across the room and I could

imagine it taking a lifetime to arrive. I avoided it without moving; it must have strayed for a long time between forgetting and remembering, unable to disappear, drifting between my indifference and my agitation.

I had just seen him and I had never seen him before,— seeing him from one minute to the next, at last, anew, for the first time; never having seen him from one look to the next, I had just understood without knowing it that I would never ever manage to look him full in the face. He was Unique. Obviously. This Obvious Fact was between him and me. I shall never know him. Him, still him, never him, never ever—terrifyingly obvious. And it was dreadfully true that this fact was becoming less obvious, it was no longer clear, it wasn't entirely him, and yet I was there before him, and from one second to the next he was there again—I had just seen him in the eternal present.

You will obviously recognize him. And what if he had changed? You will know him by your terror. By your racing pulse. Even if he wasn't the same any more? You would know him by the violent way he crashed through your waiting. In his own time, without warning. Don't wait for me, be prepared for me. I shall arrive unexpectedly. If you expect someone he won't be the one to come. Be prepared for the other, don't wait for the one who is coming, you won't know him.

Impossible to be prepared. The same old strangeness, the communal house that disturbs you; the native land where you feel an alien. The room shared with the other family. You disliked the promiscuity. The others were not your family. An old woman was going through your things. A scene was brewing. It would be a primitive scene. It was going to take place between the bed and the entrance door, between the possible and the impossible—you would have to keep the family away.

It would all happen in a few gestures, a few looks, every

silence would count. Who could have got to this deserted house—I didn't know the address—seeing it swaying I fancied it was by the sea. Who could have found me there? Despite all the things that were against The Arrival; things saying: no time, no place, no way, no clue. The door was open. Suddenly. The untidy room. You, you, at last, after all this time! His entrance!

The house was dark. The outside pressed in, behind him the air turned grey. His white hair. Yesterday it was still black, years ago. But it was him! Older, impossible. Get rid of the children, relatives, the dying, all the beings who separate, get rid of the furniture, the darkness, drive out separation. Through the visions, the surprise that was preventing you from seeing him, fight off the thought: 'that's not him.' There is no mistake. Go to him, lean against him, me against you, I wanted to weep, don't try and justify yourself, and there, leaning against his chest, love him so much, rediscover him, even if he really has changed, get through his body, get through the moment, let go of duration to seek him in the here and now. He was early. I wanted to have been waiting for him. When had he arrived? I wasn't dressed. You travelled by night then? No, no. I couldn't see how then. The day had not begun. No train, no plane, he didn't travel in time. The face altered, the eyes exceptionally clear. I was a bit startled, a bit disturbed. I am not frightened, still I am afraid. It was six o'clock. He had just arrived. I couldn't believe it. He was the one who arrives, the one who opens the door sooner than hope had hoped. He was my other chance, my life is coming to me—even if he is changed. I cling to him, let me take in my joy, while I am embracing him, with my eyes shut so that I won't see his neck, his face, so that I won't see how much each feature is resisting me, all distance was wiped out, I knew that only my blood could see. What my eyes don't see: knowing him for eternity could only take place within me. It will always be him. And I can want nothing else but the moment when he opens the door and is there.

As for the rest, that's my affair. He will get older. Younger. Taller. Thinner. I will fight off time, screens, wrinkles, doubts. I shall never see him again. I have seen him, I am seeing him, before and after time, once only.

For as long as possible, till the end.

His face. He had a black patch over one eye. I think it was the left eye. An old pain prevents me from going into details. Perhaps I only spoke to avoid looking him in the face. And yet I did look at him. Will you always be there?

His correct tone, with no kindness in it:—That's up to you.

—Don't say that, don't.

Every word terrified me.

Every moment, dread, a chance. He wore a light grey pullover. His colourless hair. The black patch over one eye. The sheets were pale grey too.

—I'll take it off later. I'll put out the light. I'll take off the bandage and I will look at you; in the night.

I explored his face, in the dark. I could hardly see. I kissed the patch, I didn't dare touch his eyes.

—Have you read the man in the mask?

Lying between his legs, huddled up in case I pressed on his chest. No. I haven't read it. Under the wool his chest with the scar across it. My longing to see it, to have seen it at last, to take it into my flesh through my eyes. A tenacious, secret longing. Show me it.

—Time to interpret the signs, is it?

Time to undress him with my hands, to reclaim from the other what is mine, to read death's letter with my eyes, in order to wipe it out.

—The man was born lucky. A covering over his head. He always had a veil in front of his eyes.

And so did I, and so did he: a curtain in front of my eyes,

draw it aside, see the edges of the wound, kiss them with my mouth.

—The veil was not torn aside until his father married him. Now—luckily— the veil would be rent. The pullover over his head, just under the breasts, a hair-line scar, I could hardly make it out, a veil of tears blurred my sight.

—The veil like a bridal veil. And yet it's nothing really. Wasn't there some mistake? He was there, I didn't need to open my eyes. The father drew the curtains aside; suddenly the child could see. The world was revealed. The clouds vanished: here was the earth. The child leant over the earth, kissed it all over. Saliva trickled out. The child laid its face on his chest, between his breasts, the child was resting.

I remember. His skin whiter than mine, his smell of a new-born child, he my child my mother my terror. His clear skin, his childhood mole, hairless, his chest completely bare, stripped bare at last. I wanted to weep. It was a discrete scar. The room was silent. That room. That was the night when anguish withdrew with the contented, natural, slow rhythm of the sea. A drowsiness arose, a steady humid breathing. Between sleeping and waking you lean over the body, you are not dreaming so you can examine the vegetation more closely, there are flowers of an unknown species growing on the chest, with long stems, countless buds, lean over the corolla, the scar is hidden, doubtless your fingers brought forth the flowers which are stopping them from stroking it. You lean over hoping that by touching the petals, smelling the flowers, you will find what is hiding from you, but will come back to you—what flowers were they, the name escapes you.

Were you in touch with the beloved's body that night?

Perhaps the flowers are snap-dragons, you said to yourself. Or else scars. Or thoughts branching out in all directions under your fingers. Leave them alone then and go to sleep. Were you in touch with silence? with the room? with the wound?

I had stopped thinking, fearing, doubting, watching,

struggling to get over the distance. I wasn't sleeping, I was asleep, I was a dream dreaming itself. I wasn't dreaming. I was listening to the silence rising, spreading round us, covering our bodies with kisses. This silence, I said to myself, is surely god watching over us.

What happened then can be told in a few words; but no one would understand: I was gazing at god the mother, his adored face, his loving, peaceful eyes. Suddenly his face convulsed, his smile went to pieces, he spat in my face, god herself spat.

His spittle on my lips, I wanted to scream, wake up. But it wasn't a dream. I was sitting on the bed. Very far away from myself, between the dense night and the night of darkness, I was passing away, the door had closed behind me again, no one can open it, I was unclean, my face filthy, the beloved's spittle on my eyes like the eagle on its prey. I was falling. I lost myself. The light too was a sea of shadows. God was howling.

The hatred in his words deafened me. My love what have you done to me? Are you Medusa? His relentless words, his frenzy filling my ears. His bitterness all over me, in my nostrils, ears, mouth, throat. I couldn't even groan, say to him: what are you doing? Murmur: what have I done?

Here is the scene: the moment I began to caress him, his bare chest, his firm body, naked, adored—it was impossible, I didn't touch him, I couldn't caress him, my fingers were paralysed.

What happened between the moment I looked at the sign traced on the breast and the moment he unleashed his terrors against me should never have happened. Time has been shattered. A moment vanished. While I was asleep. The room was silent, I was looking at his chest gleaming in the dark, I was carried away by the sight, I was looking in a dream, I was awake, I was drawing aside the veil, sleep opened out.

205

A strange cry came from him. Did I hear it? That moment has been lost.

I was sitting on the bed: on the edge of an abyss, the tide had gone out. My eyes peered into the darkness. They had trouble piercing the mass of shadows down below. My eyes bored into the dark. I finally caught sight of the bottom. I knew, immediately. I couldn't suppress a cry of horror. The cry rose out of the abyss, out of the heavy sands that lay dying below, I gasped it out over lands and doomed flesh. I had seen with my own eyes: the sea would never come back. I had seen what I should never have seen.

He cried out. A cry of pain and hatred.

Which didn't come from his lips: a scream; the breath had been crushed in his chest. He was watching me. I looked at my hand, my fingers on his chest, on the edge of the scar. A dreadul look, like a child's. What is happening to me? My love, what have you done? Are you as hard as stone? Do your fingers press heavier than the sands of the sea? The pain was so acute. It throbbed in me too. I thought I saw weals on his flank, I said to myself perhaps a vein had burst, I stroked his chest lightly to take away the pain. But under my palm, under my love, the red blotches spread wherever my hands touched; I began to scream too. The whole earth was in pain. The next moment I tore myself away from the bed. I was standing up in the strange room. My body didn't exist. I stood accused. He was asking me for an explanation. His voice full of surprised rage. How? Why? Give me a reason. I was listening. What made you do it? What am I to think of that gesture? I am listening. No excuses with me. Tell me everything. Since when? What have I done to you?

I had been listening to him for ever, I was listening to him for the first time. He had changed. It was him. God himself. One of us must die. Lost in my black thoughts I listened to him, the world's life-blood was running out.

Answer! Answer! What did you do while I was fighting?

And so you haven't changed at all? You are still the same? Not a bit different? While I was struggling? For whom? So, you are incapable of love? of understanding? of taking a hint? Couldn't you have understood? Couldn't you have trusted? You thought I was going to die? I had sworn to you. Hadn't you heard?—Horror—terror—Didn't I swear to you? No, no, yes, yes I did believe you, I did trust. But death? No faith? Yes, yes, no, no. Did your faith falter? Did you see me dead? No. Dream it, wish it, fear and loathe it? Love me, dead?

My love, listen, even now, can't you see how much you hate me? Because I didn't die. This is the treat you had in store for me is it? The first night? What have I done to you? Didn't I come back from the dead to love you? Yes. I came back: how will you forgive me for that?

My love, my fiancé, while I was resting, our first night, you couldn't stop yourself, speak, speak, there's still time, even now, I've still got time to lose for you, blood to shed for you, do I have to bleed again? Didn't I promise you? Give you everything? In advance? To the last drop? He was calling me: join me! Isn't that my one desire? But where? How? Hadn't he told you clearly? Right here? In the room? How come you can't do it? Every second thrust you further away. Didn't you want anything to do with us? His heartless voice. But his voice. And it is speaking to you. Offering the greatest joy. Don't you want to come close? Every sentence called me, pushed me away. Oh I do want, I did want, I want so much, I begged, I cried out. So you don't want to talk to me? Why don't you say so then?—You wanted to kill me off. See how I love you. Don't you want to look at yourself? What devil's got into you, making you deny, tremble? Don't you want our life together?

Was I screaming? I didn't cry out. Screams were tearing my larynx to pieces, my bronchi were smashed, my lungs frothing; if you wanted to explain yourself he wouldn't hear you, he isn't holding back his rage, his power is unleashed, how could you hope to appease him? He will be deafened by

207

your uproar; my voice ran down my throat, even if he listened my answer would not satisfy him; you want to complain, justify yourself, he was crushing me in a stormy wind, striking me, he didn't let me draw breath, no time to swallow my saliva, I was dribbling, blood pouring from my nose, a rattling in my throat—I am going to speak, just let me get my breath, 'you still refuse to say anything?'—not even a pause, a breathing space, you wanted to beg him, ask: what fault must I confess to? what crime? Tell me so I can admit it, can't you forgive me my innocence, then? My guilt. Who cried out: 'Forget me!' I'm sure it wasn't me, the pain was suffocating me, it was the sound of my voice weeping, outside me.

'You still won't say anything?' I thought I was shouting; it was my silence breaking out. Lord, who will tell me? What have I done?

You alone are the cause. It is because of you. You couldn't stop yourself could you? Did you have to touch it? That discrete scar. So you were incapable of loving it, absolutely, from afar? From the first room? The first glance? Did he have to teach me all over again? Not to go near it? Graze it with a finger nail? Breathe doubt on it?

What came over you? What hatred? Raising your hand against the man who is your life? Tearing the secret blood from the venerable flesh? Forcing the wound to speak?

—I was asleep.

—You tore my chest. Your hands are claws. Your mouth a sword blade. Who did you want to kill?

—I wasn't awake.

—You were in my arms, by my side, your hand crept up my chest, your grasping fingers clawed me. You shouldn't have dared, even in a dream.

And so, among all the possibilities that were impossible the Worst has happened? I did all I could to push him away from me, and he was giving birth, life to me; all I could to lose that life.

Didn't you have the strength to shut your eyes? To keep

208

guard over your hand while you were sleeping? To believe God's words, rather than the evidence of your senses?

And even if the worst wasn't true? In a dream or in reality? What if God had gone mad? What if he always had been mad? What if he had never been mad? What if he had decided to feign madness? Do you have the right to criticise his wish? When God pretends isn't his pretence the truth? Who are you to think you can tell the difference? Don't ask God to be you. To understand you, be like you. To have between his breasts the real trace of a real wound. He knows neither true nor false.

It was a discrete, delicate scar, actually a brush-stroke. A silence. You shouldn't have broken it. It was a Forgery, but from his own hand.

And now it is too late. No peace, no rest, no trust. No reason, no certainty, no clarity. Who can say: 'I am righteous,' before love?

When I came before him, the distance was infinite. No point in taking a plane. He had nothing more to say to me. He will never have anything to say to you. My life filled him with horror. My suffering was endless. A worm, he would trample under foot. You will perish eternally. He didn't even crush me. He went out straightaway. I was running through strange streets. From then on, I could neither find him, nor could I stop searching for him. He is not dead. He existed. Somewhere? I had no hope. Despair kept me going. Why don't you forget my gesture? Why don't you erase the scar? The vision. Stopped me living, dying, forgetting. I could not think and I couldn't stop thinking. I wasn't living. I was howling. I was terror incarnate.

No one to blot it out. No one to open the Door.

The seeds of suffering spring not out of the earth.

If you come before the Unique. His chest of pure marble. Shut your eyes. You haven't noticed anything. There is

209

nothing to notice. You have not looked at the scar. I did not gaze at it. I didn't see anything. As soon as I saw the painted line I shut my eyes. If I had seen, I would have gone mad too.

When I arrived silence had already begun. Not a word more. No one talks to me except solitude: me, suffering incarnate. I was such intense suffering, taking up time and space. This pure passion had taken over and if, far away in the depths of my soul another voice was giving me different advice, I couldn't hear it, my suffering swept everything away in its uproar. Yesterday you existed, you believed, five thousand years ago, yesterday. An hour before I existed, I believed in myself, not a moment ago I was called Hélène— you will never believe it ever again. There was an explosion. No past left.

I couldn't remember. Who told you about it? Perhaps He did, or you heard by chance. Nothing left. The accident. Nothing happening any more. I only knew the (F)act. I didn't dwell on it. I wasn't thinking of anything. I couldn't reject the (F)act. I couldn't admit it. It was true. The All-Present told you so. No escape. No disbelief. I had to believe. And so what is untrue may be true. We were in the last room. It was me. I was in a plane. I was crazed with pain. Perhaps it wasn't Him. But He still had all the love in his keeping. I hadn't taken anything away from him. The earth was swelling, seas were rising and freezing—the gap was widening. Suffering rose above it, left its mark and seared my spine. Demanded explanations.

Blood-suckers in my flesh right down to the bone. I was gnawed by leprosy from the tips of my toes to my eyelids. There was the new (F)act. Only he could explain.

I was sitting on a heap of ashes and dung. Explain to me. I'll accept it. Once I could have spoken for him. Who can tell me about the (F)act, but Him?

My body clothed in vermin, a wound starting to bleed on the chest under the breasts. My dress soaked in poison. Explain to me. What harm did I do you? What wound did I

210

open? I loved him as much as ever, my life con-fused with the breath of His voice. Reunion in a hurricane. My violence broke out. I screamed: What do you want of me? When will you break your silence? Do you want my life, death? Decide, name what you want. My fury matching his silence. All the force of the elements, all the passions of life, the fires of hell, of love were feeding one single desire that was consuming me: that he should tell me, probe the wound, reveal my fault, before death. Dumb, not a word—who will make him spit it out?

My words shook the walls, the room was quaking, the ground was undermined. I wasn't talking, I exploded, thundered, spat out the words, roared, making a deafening noise, maddening everyone. There was universal uproar. Seas hurled themselves upon the land. The land fled, pillars supporting cities collapsed. Three or four words were revolving crazily in my mind, too fast to settle. Not a word. He was lying stretched out on the bed, his adored face, the black patch, his habitual calm. The row I was making bored him. Wearied him. His tight-lipped smile: you will never get in.

And what if god were mad? I would love her to distraction. He was mad, he was wisdom itself. His calm in the face of my frenzy meant to me: 'I have never met you.' How do you know? You don't speak his silent language. Would you dare interpret it?

I didn't ask: 'What about the room, the promise, the duel, the promise, the truth? . . . What about the waiting, the triumph, the wound, the scar? . . . the black patch, the truth, the trust? . . .

Howling drowned my voice.

I didn't say: 'You are treating me like a criminal. And yet you know my innocence, my guilt. Does my suffering amuse you? I can't understand you. I don't want to understand you.' His silence struck me—dumb.

If you hadn't been howling so loudly you might have

managed to find the strength to slip behind his silence. That's why I yelled. To avoid coming close to an answer. I didn't want to risk coming within reach of the truth.

I didn't want to say: 'You pulled me out of death, you handed me over to death. If you are not Death, who are you then? I didn't say it, but I thought it. I kept it secret for fear of losing madness. Leave it alone. Go away. You will think about it later. On your way back. After the very last moment. If you ceased to understand the Incomprehensible you wouldn't be able to accept it.

The day of the execution you were *absolutely* desolate. Those who haven't gone through it cannot imagine it. It is such a Great Pain. Maddening: you must somehow take in your death in a single day. How easy all other losses are compared to this one! Simple, because you have time to take them in, live them, bear them. But in this case you must put yourself to death: put mind, life, suffering to death.

I should have thought about it sooner, gone through it before. Made quite a different day of it. Planned it. I never dreamt of it. Nothing led me to this fate. Nothing is mis-leading: it is precisely 'Nothing' that is leading you to this fate. It had been written.

(My fingers digging into his flesh, ripping the silk, skin tearing at matter, searching for the wound, scratching, going through the blood to get back to the roots. My fingers didn't touch, didn't come near, didn't know the chest, didn't find the wound. I never wished for his death, if I had, it would have killed me, but I wouldn't have wanted him to die, but I wasn't sure, that could mean something quite different; I didn't confess; I said: I have forgotten. But if I had wanted to remember I wouldn't have forgotten. If I had forgotten how could I not remember? I am sure I didn't commit that act. That certainty could not be based on Nothing. It certainly wasn't a mistake. I didn't confess, I admitted, I didn't admit, I didn't deny. That was my fault. A mistake, and yet the truth. I wanted to tell the truth. I wanted to get to the real truth. As if the secret of the Real Truth wasn't false; or rather, as if what was really true wasn't secretly false. Don't tell the truth: if you did it would cease to be true. I couldn't go on living without dying.)

I had kept cool. When you are condemned to death what other decision can you make? Not to live your last moments? So cool. Alas! Icy. All thoughts paralysed by the shock. Blood clotted. Never mind. You have to accommodate the huge thing, whole, inside your body. I was at home. In deadly sorrow. But calm. I was putting myself to death.

Life was so short. Don't think of anything. I wasn't thinking of anything. Then I thought about the day after. Without me. The story I shall not hear. What might not have happened to me. Life, chance. How simple everything is for me: all I had to do was to die.

The head falls. In front of me: the knife blade. My aim, my job: to cut. The time had come. Afterwards it will all be over. Afterwards? Can't be pictured without . . . Suddenly the spectacular explosion of life in my head. Suddenly time comes back into being, its brief span, the threat: not to have done anything, thought anything, said anything, left anything behind—nothing. Suddenly the one final gesture: call him, him, my life, my hate, my beloved, my terror. His voice, his voice, one last time!

Call him? Who? With what voice? With what silence?

You say: 'Pure is my soul, I am unsullied.' What god would believe that? To whom would you cry out? To whom would you turn, begging. You don't even know his real name. If he answered your call, who would come to your aid? Because he wantonly multiplied his Presence and he had countless names. Call him by the last name, my god, tell me where to reach you, what memory would recapture you? What letter would stop you? Quick: my two books of names and the new ones, and in the two, my two notebooks, and in the notebooks the old names and the new, and in the names his thousands of names, his names everywhere, all the names are his name and not one succeeds in naming him. You want to have Verbal intercouse with that Silence? What a laugh.

It was just then, ten minutes before death that the Idea occurred to me. The one that only occurs just before: escape is only possible when the present is at an end. When you have already become a memory. You re-called yourself—to life.

Run away? As soon as the Idea occurred I rushed to save myself. To stop my ears in case he had the Idea of calling me back. Fear it. Desire it. Get away. He won't re-call you. But you will never know. Run away? And no more waiting, so no more terror? No more voice, no more silence? No more dying of fear in case he isn't listening, in case he is, in case he's coming. Run away. What can I lose? Aren't I already dead, any-way.

Such an instant decision: walls topple down, you give an order, the door is wiped out, you change destiny without warning. The stairs, I shouted! Instantly—their marble landings, their flights, their floods of crazy steps. I hardly moved. Space sprang to meet me, the way-out was coming nearer. Had the time come? I looked like a completely ordinary woman. The staircase was narrowing, filling up, I didn't run down, I dived from top to bottom. Space melted away, the steps were tumbling down, mountains moved aside, seas parted, the stair-well was already flooded with cops, the order had been given, the sun would not come out, I charged along, head down, slipped through the cops, cleaved the air, it was a September morning, a few steps lower down the earth had caved in, I began to hop along the crest of the abyss, words

214

stared at me—is it her?—lost!—no, it's not her—saved!—one more chasm, a pass, down the bannisters, outside in a flash, in a minute, the last, they'll be in the room upstairs. That very minute outside, really outside, I am running along, buoyant, head up.

I didn't weep, I didn't stop the tears streaming down, I went out, cars were dancing along, taxis passing, tears flowing, and so life goes on, I thought, I turned round several times, the marble steps were screened, going out of (my) sight, were still frighteningly there, but hidden, I set off at the speed of life.

No, I didn't weep, the tears were flowing despite me. I was intoxicated, I could see, I could see myself, and I could see myself a-new—from the first door to the last step.

If you don't die heart-broken from so much anguish you will have to think the unthinkable. You will have your Chance: you will actually have to choose between a different life and death. You are one of those who have gone astray and come out on the other side. A path vanished. You are one of those beings who have really worshipped the Strange One, whom you can never approach—except by going so far away from yourself that you come to the room of no-return.

I reached that room. I came back from it, strange. Between the moment of entering and the moment of returning the impossible takes place. You contemplate god, you look him in the face, and god does not exist.

That is why what happens in there may just as well not take place.

Then comes the moment of return from the land of no-return: Where? You can't say you're home, not really. It was so far away from me, in a remote time and space. And yet I was really home, in my mother's house to be precise. That's the effect it has, always the same, despite so many years, an enormously devastating effect and yet, strangely, not dis-agreeable. Because it can't happen to me any more now. And yet it does happen continually, with extraordinary violence, every day, it is him, his grave face, if it isn't him, who else would it be?

The scene can always take place this way: when you are on the point of thinking: 'It's strange, everyone comes back, except him. All those I have forgotten have returned, and he hasn't come back once in so many years;' the moment you are about to say that to yourself, when it is more than certain that he will never come back. In that case and in that case only, he may come back. Because he cannot return until it has become completely impossible: when you feel nothing but indifference and aversion, yes, when you don't feel the distance, nor when you do feel distanced, then, there is a chance, for he is Distance itself. And he's already there. When you distance yourself from him you give him the chance to come; don't wait for him, forget him, lose him in your memory: it's him, his influence.

He had come to visit.

—And so, I thought, it's over. I can see death without dying?—Playing cat and mouse. The roles were ambiguous. I wasn't the mouse any more and he, god, was a mixture of the two. He was a man heavy as death, light as death, who smiled to himself. He had shrunk to normal size. The whole time he was passing through I felt a distant ironic smile hovering on my lips. It amused me to see him as I had before. There was a hint of terror in my smile. You don't face his madness without fearing to be bewitched. You have changed. He doesn't know. He hadn't changed. You can be certain. God is always the same. There is the room. Where he goes on killing you off.

And here, during the whole scene, time splits up, the scene doesn't go by, it goes on, it had gone on yesterday, in another time, yes, all the time what is going on doesn't seem to be taking place here, doesn't seem to be happening, to be running on, as it did every day in the past; but it seems to be flowing in advance into the future, where I am now, amazed to contemplate my madness in person. I exclaimed: 'And so I saw him again! Who would have thought it? There is one being in the world of whom you say: I'll never see him again alive. And that's him!' I was looking at him seeing me again, where I no longer am. That scene caused me a secret pleasure.

A secret pleasure that went deep: the scene took its time, gave me time. Little by little let yourself be drawn in, you could step back, let yourself be sucked in, there will be time to draw back, let yourself come close, you'll only have to shut your eyes—the past can no longer give you a Present of its pain. There is no delight more poignant than the memory of Great Suffering. My heart is wrung with joy. If he could come back, anything can happen. You can think that one day-night the unique, that can only happen once, will happen once again, he will come back, he will be there, your madness—as *it* will never come back. In the fullness of terror. The scene will take place in a room you have never entered. The conversation was going on. You are standing before him. Almost alone. His presence on the bed couldn't really bridge the gap. He asked for me. As before, today, as always. Spreading like wild fire through your veins. How could I deny? This havoc, this grace? How could I fail to name the need, acknowledge it. Since that's how it is. That love beyond love. Despite myself. Do you want more?

I want it, eternally, despite myself, despite my hurt. His way of bringing life, death, within reach, only within reach. You can still avoid him—I can face him now.

I can climb the marble stairs without hesitating, go back over all the roads, meet ancestors and descendants, receive every letter again, not one has gone astray, I can read them without trembling; haven't I learnt not to let myself be intimidated by the incomprehensible, learnt to climb in the dark, without expectation, without hope, without despair, without ever losing my fear—that all-surpassing joy.

I climbed barefoot so I could go faster, to enjoy the feel of the icy marble; I climbed right up to the last step, as high as

217

possible, light flooded out, the staircase was soon bathed in a humid, cool light which seemed to make the steps well up under my feet, dissolve them, sweep them away and it is another, still me, who is climbing outside me, going on, carried away by that powerful uncertainty that is still there, still exhilarating, promising, luring me as I am rushed along by this love, this sweet threat.

Suddenly, no more steps, no more walls, I am before memory's room; no more door, suddenly no more past, no memory, I haven't *returned*, I was on the point of *arriving*, I thought: 'Oh you, who made yourself invisible before my eyes, I am coming,' the moment is approaching, I was going to look him in the face, at last, I would see him, I was going to see him—disappear. That will be the time to look him in the face. He was lying down, his face so strangely dear to me; I was frightened, I admired his calm, he was exposed, his right eye staring into my left eye unblinking. I didn't take my right eye off the black hymen that covered his left eye. He wasn't hiding, he let me contemplate the truth, his appearance, he let my eyes caress such a tranquil absence, I would never know him, it would be him, I would never have understood him, my ignorance would increase, I revelled in it. I loved him as never before. Then I loved him: mad, unknown—gone.

I loved his calm radiance, his way of not running away, not staying, not closing his eye. The way he was resting there eternally, on the bed which would never be a marriage bed; letting a smile flicker over his face and fade away, the expression of an unshakeable, absolutely indifferent wisdom; so certain. I am not needed. His impassive presence; split off, apart, the emanation of an absence that didn't insist, that simply affirmed. I was on the point of worshipping his madness: it made me feel I may as well not have existed. I saw the light. I saw so clearly that I saw everything, I was seeing nothing, I was seeing no-body. Yes, I saw! I saw myself too. Through the eyes of the mad god. That vision at point blank range. Laughter tore me apart. I sat down on the top step, absolutely alone, I was escaping, anguish pouring out of my throat, I am losing, letting myself go, it was a new kind of anguish, a keen joy, I was casting off my body; I must have laughed for hours, ruinous laughter ravaging my flesh. I began to spit blood. I spewed up my story from the very first moment. That joyful laughter is clearing me out, wiping my heart clean. Relieved me.

I got rid of god. I finally threw up love. Nothing left but the bared soul. How clean I was, how purified, wrung dry. I had lost sight, body, faith; you are saved! You can wait for the next life without impatience, without thinking ahead. Don't bother to wait for it. If you wait it'll be there already. It is coming. Who could stop it? There is no one left. And that certainly inspires an acute delight, a twinge of anguish that excites you, that touch of terror that makes the heart start beating again when you have just died. I didn't love any more, I didn't have to love any-body. It was love loving; whom I love.

19 June, 1976